MAYDAY, MAYDAY, MAYDAY!
SPIN INSTRUCTIONS PLEASE!

A DECADE OF THE BEST AVIATION CARTOONS
by
Bob Stevens

Dedication

This book is dedicated to that endangered species—general aviation pilots and enthusiasts—who are pressing on, in spite of overpowering bureaucracy and spiralling costs.

A DECADE OF THE BEST AVIATION CARTOONS
by
Bob Stevens

AERO
A division of TAB BOOKS Inc.
Blue Ridge Summit, PA

FIRST EDITION

FIRST PRINTING

Printed and published in the United States of America by Aero, a division of TAB
BOOKS Inc.

Library of Congress Cataloging-in-Publication Data

Stevens, Bob, 1923-
   Mayday, Mayday, Mayday! : spin instructions please / by Bob
Stevens.
     p. cm.
   ISBN 0-8306-8964-8 (pbk)
    1. Private flying—Caricatures and cartoons. 2. American wit and
humor, Pictorial. I. Title.
NC1429.S64A4 1989
741.5'973—dc20   89-14993
                                    CIP

TAB BOOKS Inc. offers software for sale. For information and a catalog, please
contact TAB Software Department, Blue Ridge Summit, PA 17294-0850.

Questions regarding the content of this book should be addressed to:

**Reader Inquiry Branch
TAB BOOKS Inc.
Blue Ridge Summit, PA 17294-0214**

Acquisitions Editor: Jeff Worsinger
Book Editor: Norval G. Kennedy
Production: Katherine Brown

Foreword

When you see a Bob Stevens cartoon, you often see the real Bob Stevens, too. That's not to say that Bob is a one-dimensional cartoon character, but rather that he frequently portrays himself as one of the subjects in the cartoon, often as the "Dilbert" who is doing a dumb thing. See the pilot with the wispy mustache and the sweat drops pouring off his brow because the propeller has stopped? That's Bob.

Bob Stevens cartoons himself because he's probably been in just the same kind of situation. He knows exactly how much "pucker factor" is created when an engine quits running. He knows firsthand the embarrassment of screwing up a flight procedure in front of your peers. And fortunately for the rest of us, Bob Stevens has always been able to turn a tale of disaster into a delightfully funny lesson. That's because Bob can see the humor in virtually any situation.

After Bob and Barbara moved to a new home in a part of the country noted for its heavy doses of liquid sunshine, Bob called about two months later to tell us how it had rained for 63 days in a row and had only stopped raining when it started to snow. His airplane, he reported, was currently under six feet of snow and was recognizable only as a lump somewhere on the field. Most people would be crying the blues in a similar situation, but not Bob; we got to laughing so hard about it that I'm sure we overloaded the telephone line.

Another time, same airplane, I volunteered to help Bob change its oil and filter. On the Mooney 201, the oil filter is virtually inaccessible on the back of the engine. By the time we got it off, we'd dumped oil all over the back of the engine compartment, onto the ground and all over our shoes. Again, we achieved a laughter overload. After that, all Bob had to do was mention "oil change" and it would cause ripples of mirth.

The monthly "Caption Contest" in *Private Pilot* magazine was another laugh-a-second production. The magazine staff would meet with Bob at a convenient restaurant to read and judge reader entries for the feature. With out loud reading of "Listen to this one. . ." or "Here's the worst . . .," we giggled and roared our way through stacks of entries.

Bob loves humor, as can be seen in any of his cartoons. But he loves funny stories just as much as visual art, and there's always the phone call from him with the latest: "I just heard this one at the QB meeting, and I knew you'd like it too . . ." and we'd exchange the latest gags amidst howls of laughter.

I'm convinced that there are people in this world whose mission is to bring joy to others. After nearly two decades of mirthful association with Bob Stevens, I'm convinced that he's the leader of the funny squadron.

Dennis Shattuck
Editorial Director
Kitplanes and Private Pilot

Acknowledgments

The author acknowledges with thanks the following publications and persons who made this book possible:

Private Pilot, Dennis Shattuck, Editorial Director
Callback, NASA's Aviation Safety Reporting System newsletter
IFR "On the Air," Jeffery Parnau, editor
CAF Dispatch, Confederate Air Force, Harlingen, Texas
AG-Pilot International, F. Sherertz, contributor
"*Say Again*," Martin Leeuwis, author, the Netherlands

And countless friends, acquaintances, and just plain friendly folks who have contributed ideas to the author in 40-plus years of flying.

Introduction

Humor is a delicate commodity. Handled with a heavy hand it will shatter and become vitriolic, sarcastic, and even morose—the very antithesis of its namesake. I call non-humorous drawings that make a point "jugular vein" cartoons. Subjects like safety—crashes or accidents "going-someplace-to-happen"—usually fall into this category. As one political cartoonist said: "If you aim your pen at the jugular vein it can bounce back and skewer you." That's the risk some cartoonists take to make a point.

On the other hand, humor treated with a delicate touch can be immensely funny and rewarding. It leaves the viewer laughing and light-hearted. That's what it's all about.

Hopefully, you'll find a lot of the latter in this book, which is a collection of nearly a decade of the best cartoons from my feature "Stop Squawk" in *Private Pilot* magazine. If you see yourself and friends in these cartoons, I've hit the mark. If not, the book makes an excellent paperweight or doorstop.

Bob Stevens
Fallbrook, California
1988

The "Aviation Glossary" you see on the opposite and subsequent pages just popped into my mind years ago when I started drawing for *Air Force* Magazine. It's origin—as far as I know—was in prose from the Confederate Air Force's booklet entitled simply, "Aviation Glossary." Where the CAF got the material, I know not. But like most aviation humor, its genesis can be traced almost to the Wright Brothers' Model B. The good stuff never dies.

Other drolleries on the page might have come through military channels. But, what the hey, when you've been drawing aviation humor 40-plus years you take anything you get—as long as you don't commit outright plagiarism.

Note: The bird in the lower left-hand corner was my first aircraft—a 1972 Bellanca Super Viking. What a sweet machine! Those 300 horses up front felt like a P-51's Merlin! The fabric, however, did not take kindly to many years of sitting outside in all kinds of weather.

REMEMBER? YOUR FIRST SOLO CROSS COUNTRY? YOU'VE JUST DROPPED THE PLOTTER, YOU'RE *TWO* MIN. OVERDUE AT YOUR LAST CHECK POINT, YOU ONLY HAVE **1** HR FUEL REMAINING PLUS A COCKPIT FULL OF THE WRONG MAP, ETC., ETC....

MUST HAVE A CROSS WIND NUTHIN' LOOKS FAMILIAR

WHAT'S THE RECIPROCAL OF 030? WHERE'S MY E6B? *GEEZ!* *WHY* AM I UP HERE?

AVIATION GLOSSARY

ALTIMETER SETTING: Where the altimeter sets. Usually behind the control column on a near-minimums instrument approach.

BANGER ON DOWN-WIND, THIS IS PATMAR TOWER. MAKE A LEFT 360 TO GAIN ONE MINUTE FOR TRAFFIC SPACING

PATMAR TOWER THIS IS BANGER 63 ROMEO. FOR YOUR INFORMATION IT TAKES *TWO* MINUTES TO MAKE A 360!

ROGER BANGER 63 ROMEO, THEN MAKE A **180** AND *BACK IN!*

The story about the poor clown out of fuel is one of my favorites; I use it in my speech patter. (That's the material you throw together when asked to give a talk at some aviation gathering.) It has never failed to get a big laugh. I can understand why some people want to be stand-up comics because waiting for the roar of laughter that you know will come when delivering the punch line is a delicious moment!

An old WWII instructor pilot told me this event *actually* happened at Hemet, California. I later found out that (1) Hemet was a primary flying school and (2) primary trainers had no radios. So much for the authenticity of the story! I had to update the gag anyway, so I merely put the student in a more modern trainer, which *has* to be equipped with a radio to go anyplace these days.

AVIATION GLOSSARY

Blind Flying Hood: An inebriated gangster-type aviator.

Everyone connected with aviation knows what happened after the president fired a goodly number of our air traffic controllers—it was a zoo out there in "airtrafficland." Just when things seemed to be getting better, there was a series of real and imagined midairs. The Washington bureaucracy reacted in true knee-jerk fashion; more regulations, less uncontrolled airspace, and additional work for the overburdened controllers. No wonder they went from a 120 words-a-minute delivery to just under the speed of light!

The bottom "hopping" cartoon, done many years ago, shows what can happen to a cartoonist when he buys material. I threw this in to show how a gag, which is really "not you," can stand out like a sore thumb. (If you like it better than my own stuff, shown above, I'm in *deep* trouble!) I don't buy material any more.

AND HERE'S A "ROYAL ORDER OF THE PURPLE SHAFT" AWARD TO THOSE CLOWNS IN GROUND CONTROL OR CLEARANCE DELIVERY-OR WHEREVER- WHO GIVE YOU YOUR IFR CLEARANCE AS IF THEY ARE BEING PAID BY THE NUMBER OF WORDS PER SECOND—

I threw in these pages on flying in Mexico knowing full well that many readers have not and will not fly there, but people read travel brochures of places they'll never see, don't they?

Since these pages were drawn, a lot of things have changed in the nation to our south: the monetary rate of exchange and the price of avgas, just to mention two. The peso has gone from something like 20 to the dollar to around 2,000 to one and avgas from around 30 cents a gallon to about $1.30 (at this writing).

The reference of five minutes from Mexican to U.S. Customs refers primarily to ports of entry between California and Mexico.

My wife and I flew to Mexico many times and thoroughly enjoyed ourselves. Certain times and places in Mexico are best not remembered, however, just like a lot of foreign countries.

FLYING IN MEXICO
(OR, DON'T GET "MONTEZUMA'S REVENGE" AT 6500')

THE WATER IN THIS ENCHANT-ING LAND HAS BEEN KNOWN TO PRODUCE THE 'TOURISTAS'. MIX THIS WITH THE DISTANCES BETWEEN PAVED STRIPS *and* IT'S DY-NO-MITE!

DON'T FORGET DENSITY ALTITUDE. MANY STRIPS ARE HIGH, DRY--*and* SHORT. FLYING THROUGH THE LOCAL CANTINA CAN RUIN YOUR WHOLE DAY—

"FLIGHT WATCH" IS REALLY 122.9 (PLANE-TO-PLANE)... LISTEN TO THE BIRDS AHEAD- YOU'LL GET IT STRAIGHT & *NOW*

ALSO, TANK-UP (FUEL, THAT IS) BE-FORE LEAVING - BUT REMEMBER YOU MAY BE LANDING AGAIN IN ABOUT 5 MIN. FOR U.S. CUSTOMS. (IT COULD BE A GEAR-BENDING EXPERIENCE!)

We actually saw an unthinking couple try the stunt shown in the upper left-hand corner. The plane was an already "loaded-to-the-hilt" Twin Comanche. The pilot, who was stressed out, finally put his foot down. Last time we saw the pots and the bull they marked the east end of the runaway at Morelia.

The Twin Beech shown here was our second airplane. A vintage Baron painted yellow—*all* yellow. Hughes Air West's DC-9s were painted the same color and were referred to by tower operators as "bananas." We, of course, were "Chiquita banana." The day I picked up the bird avgas hit a buck a gallon. (That was *a lot* in 1980 dollars!) We didn't keep it long.

FLYING IN MEXICO

Restrain your passengers from picking up "bargains" (like clay pottery) as souvenirs—unless, of course, you're flying a DC-3.

Remember, there's no single engine night or instrument flying permitted (for good reasons!)

Nav aids in the hinterlands can be a bit sketchy...

Ye olde iron compass (there are more of 'em than paved roads)

Better have your conversion factors (liters-gals / pesos-$) down pat—things can get pretty frantic at the gas pumps.

Thousands of A & Ps out there have probably been tempted to react like the mechanic shown at the top of the page opposite. Pilots are notorious for giving vague analysis of in-flight mechanical or radio malfunctions. This is particularly frustrating to a mechanic who cannot ride along (e.g., a single-place bird) to hear for himself sounds that go "bump-in-the-flight."

The cartoon of the little low-wing about to be swallowed by the big jet borders on the "jugular vein" drawing discussed in the Foreword. There's just enough improbability to the gag to keep it from slipping into the macabre . . . it's a fine line.

MECHANICS: HERE'S HOW TO SEND THOSE VAGUE PILOTS TO THE FUNNY FARM:

The Aviation Glossary box will pretty much disappear from the pages of this book. This little ''feature within a feature'' became so popular in *Private Pilot* that I figured it might be the theme for a book. I gathered all those printed to date, dug out my trusty copy of the CAF (Confederate Air Force) *Aviation Glossary* and, with the help of a few talented contributors, assembled 96 pages into a booklet entitled *Prop Wash*. It must have struck a nerve with general aviation enthusiasts—*Prop Wash* is now in its Fifth printing. (End of plug).

The reader will find similar cartoons illustrated in the pages that follow. The ''Illustrated Aviation/Pilot's Glossary/Dictionary'' and ''ICAO Alphabet Game'' are typical. These are merely camouflaged versions of the *Prop Wash* theme. It's really a lazy man's way of cartooning—all the artist has to do is visualize and draw a known label or saying.

Basic instruments can be especially trying with a snotty CFII

These terms are well known to aviators—the context they are shown in is not. The "Flying Off the Handle" didn't register with many readers when it first appeared, until they studied the map. It shows, of course, the panhandles of Texas and Oklahoma.

I bought my first airplane, a Bellanca Super Viking, in Plainview, Texas. The thrill of owning my very *own* aircraft was eclipsed by running out of battery soon thereafter because the pitot heat was left in the "on" position. Moral: read the pilot's manual before checking out in *any* bird!

ILLUSTRATED AVIATION GLOSSARY

FLARE OUT

FLYING OFF THE HANDLE

FEATHERING A PROP

"FOLLOW ME THROUGH"

The different terminology used in "precision" and "nonprecision" approaches, as covered in the FAA IFR written exam (which is the toughest I've ever taken), has confused more than one applicant. We had lots of tricky memory aids. The only one I can remember is "precision-decision," e.g., only in the precision approach (ILS, GCA, LDA, etc.) is the term *decision* height given. That's the altitude below which you will probably bust your fanny if you don't have the proper things in view. A lot of people are not with us today because they ignored this very basic rule.

PITCH SETTING
(SELF EXPLANATORY)

PRECISION APPROACH

ONE WHEREIN YOU <u>FIND</u> THE FIELD ON YOUR VERY FIRST TRY.

NON-PRECISION APPROACH

ONE WHERE YOU MUST LAND TO ASK THE LINE BOY WHERE YOU ARE.

MINOR REPAIR

THOSE DONE BY A 16 YEAR OLD.

As anyone who has visited that enchanted land south of the border knows, the middle panel ''holding short'' can be painfully true. There are all kinds of remedies for you *after* being stricken with ''Montezuma's Revenge,'' ''The Mexican Two-Step'' or plain ol' ''trots,'' but I have yet to find a real good *preventative*. Staying away from the water helps, but a sneaky ice cube can get you. A flight surgeon I took on a trip deep into Baja swore by a swig of Pepto Bismol every morning to ward off the evil amoebas—it worked for him, I was a basket case.

ILLUSTRATED AVIATION GLOSSARY

" TAKING OFF IN A TIZZY "

" DIRTYING UP THE AIRCRAFT "

"HOLDING SHORT"

"CHOPPING THE THROTTLE"

"ONCE AROUND THE FLAGPOLE"

When this panel was drawn, the loans for aircraft at 18 percent were considered very high, so you can see that this particular page was not done yesterday. I'm not exactly sure what the current rate for loans is, but I'd bet a bundle that some are higher that 18 percent.

Most of the cartoons I've done throughout my aviation career have been what you might call "family rated." The downwind leg blurb is just about as racy as I'll get in cartooning, because by and large most of the publications I've drawn for have youngsters in the family that could pick up the magazines. I'm not a bluenose—that's just the audience I draw to.

Nine pilots out of 10 could give you the definition of the bottom panel without looking at "heated air mass." Hangar flying is one of the oldest forms of aviatin' in the business.

PILOT'S UNABASHED DICTIONARY

STEEP BANK

DOWNWIND LEG

LAZY 8

HEATED AIR MASS

Anyone who doesn't recognize Hugh Hefner's Playboy Bunny on "Hotel Romeo" just hasn't been by a newsstand in the last 30 years. I understand that the interior of this bird had some pretty exotic furnishings.

The term "Lima Kilo" doesn't leave a whole lot to the imagination when you can read the packages inside the aircraft. However, there is a little misdirection on the tail of the aircraft. Sharp observers will notice that the numbers of the aircraft have been obliterated and the call sign LK is the only thing visible. If you think this guy is hauling prunes, you better look again.

"November Sierra" needs a little explanation for those people who live in the flat lands. The mountains in the background are obviously the Sierra Nevadas and probably should have been labeled as such, but I just hate putting labels on things. I once had a cartoonist friend who labeled almost everything he drew. If he drew a picture of the world, he would label it "The World." A wiseacre came up and said to him one day, "I'm sure glad you labeled that thing because I thought it was a basketball." Back to the drawing—any poor devil trying to fly over the Sierras in a November snowstorm would probably come out the other side looking like a popsicle.

THE ICAO ALPHABET GAME

HOTEL
ROMEO

LIMA
KILO

TANGO
FOXTROT

NOVEMBER
SIERRA

"Uniform Bravo" is mislabeled. It should be "Uniform Crazy" because any idiot that would try to fly in conditions depicted is flat out of his gourd. Unfortunately, there is no ICAO abbreviation for crazy.

The blurb entitled "Delta Echo" plays on Delta Airline's theme. Unfortunately, the reverse of the scene depicted is sometimes true and the heavy iron people have given general aviation a hard time in some of our crowded airports. The first aircraft behind the Delta airliner is a picture of my little Mooney 201. The Mooney was my third and last wholly-owned aircraft. She was a beauty. I loved her and stuck her in as many cartoons as I could without becoming *too* obvious.

"Whiskey Victor" at the bottom of the page is a very brief flying safety message. I don't try to lecture in my cartoons but there's only one thing more stupid than flying under the influence of alcohol and that is taking a drug snort before trying to fly.

THE ICAO ALPHABET GAME

UNIFORM BRAVO

ROMEO PAPA

DELTA ECHO

WHISKEY VICTOR

The name on the door in the upper left-hand panel is that of the flight surgeon I referred to several pages previously. A medical examiner and former pilot, he is a friend of mine and we flew together on several long trips. Like a lot of other cartoonists, I can't resist sticking friends in cartoons. The reason that you cannot read his name clearly is because it might be that Old Doc is in a place now where someone could track him down for nefarious reasons.

The ''urge to kill'' panel in the lower right-hand corner depicts a situation that any pilot can relate to. Any noise other than the routine sound of the engine and background radio chatter can immediately get your attention. To have someone yell, ''Oh Look'' or ''Look Out'' can be heartstopping. As the old saw puts it, ''A midair can ruin your whole day.''

THE URGE TO KILL –

You're in a heavy traffic area and your earthling psgr spots a familiar landmark points and shouts, *"OH LOOK!"*

(You can always plead justifiable homicide – no judge who's a pilot will convict you)

The upper three panels are a wish-dream for me. I was never able to get my mother into an airplane with me—as a matter of fact, I think there are very few airplanes that she's *ever* gotten into. It always seems that when you're trying to do your best, everything turns to manure. I pulled this same stunt with my wife soon after getting my ticket, and her only comment was: "Honey, do you always land that way?"

The theme, "You know it's going to be a rotten day when . . ." comes from several well known pocketbooks of the same name. It's a fairly simple thing to dig material from these books by just relating them to aviation.

I have a whole page of nutty mnemonics that someday I intend to illustrate. This particular one seemed appropriate as the cartoon appeared in the middle of winter.

You know it's going to be a rotten day when...

You're over rough terrain, the mill swallows a valve — you yell "Mayday" at center and they come back...

NUTTY MNEMONICS

ODD PEOPLE FLY EAST *

* ESPECIALLY IN SLEET and FREEZING RAIN !

Readers will recall that back in the early '80s, soon after the president fired all the striking air traffic controllers, we had barely controlled chaos in the air for a few days. When things settled down, a system of "reservations" was set up to handle IFR flight plans. The system was flawed—as many systems are in our bureaucratic set-up—but it, on the whole, handled the "must go" traffic.

The "window" that is described in No. 3 panel was just that. If you were *one* minute early or *one* minute late, you would not be accepted by the system. They had limited computer capacity to handle the job, which prompted a lot of hustled takeoffs and landings because of this arrangement.

COPING WITH THE NEW FAA IFR RESERVATIONS SYSTEM

1 FILE *EARLY*...

...TO ENSURE YOUR PLACE IN THE SYSTEM.

2. NO "POP-UP" CLEARANCES WILL BE ACCEPTED!

3. *DON'T BE LATE!* THE 30 MIN. "WINDOW" IS ONLY OPEN THAT LONG—BRIEF YOUR PASSENGERS!

Continuing with the subject of the new FAA system implemented after the air traffic controllers' strike, the void created by the absence of these people necessitated bringing in substitute controllers immediately. Many of the controllers were from the military. As the poor soul in the upper left-hand corner will attest, not all of these controllers used standard phraseology. I can remember one poor fella' wandering around Ontario Airport getting in everybody's way because he was on the wrong frequency or didn't understand the phraseology. Finally, in desperation, he stopped and queried the tower with, "What do you *want* me to do?" That prompted the reply, "I want you to *listen up*, Mister!"

The scene of the pilot out over the desert getting his clearance for approach was not too far from the truth. On several occasions I can recall being out over the Salton Sea some 80 to 100 miles east of San Diego and getting a clearance to start my descent. There just weren't enough people to go around in the early phases of this trauma.

COPING WITH THE NEW FAA RESERVATIONS SYSTEM

The title, "Just Before It Hit the Fan . . ." came from an old series of cartoons I used to do for a travel magazine; they became highly adaptive to aviation situations. All a reader has to do is close his or her eyes and imagine how the second picture would appear.

In the case of the hotshot coming out of the blocks, he's going to be minus a tail cone.

The guy fueling the aircraft on the ladder is going to end up suspended by the hose.

You *know* what is going to happen to the guy painting the pinstripe on the aircraft.

I wouldn't want to be in the shoes of the big mouth that just parked in the heavy iron's allocated spot.

The frightening thing about this page is that almost all of the situations depicted can happen and have happened to people.

JUST BEFORE IT HIT THE FAN...

Communications—or the lack thereof—I maintain, has been the under-pinning strength of aviation humor since the dawn of flight. I've noticed that about 90 percent of all humor involves the garbled word and/or mis-interpretation of the straight word.

Again, in the lower sequence I inserted my favorite airplane, the Mooney 201. I distinctly recall a conversation between a Texas controller and myself that pretty much followed the scenario you see here.

COMMUNICATIONS - OR THE LACK THEREOF:

SOMEBODY'S GOT A TRANSMITTER THAT SOUNDS LIKE A STEPPED-ON CAT —

SCREEEEEE!

A LOCAL TOWER TRAINEE MANFULLY STEPS IN —

ALL AIRCRAFT IN THE LOCAL AREA — TURN OFF YOUR TRANSMITTERS!

?

OKAY!

NOW TURN 'EM BACK ON ...

YOU'VE BEEN TRYING TO GET A CLEARANCE FROM A MUSHY-MOUTHED CONTROLLER —

AH SAY *AGIN* ... MOANEY 201 GOLF QUEBEC IS CLEARED TO th mumble INTERSECTION ti-mumble. ... *and* THANZ TO TH' ili·· WHEEZ ···ih MAINTIAN ···· TO THE ·:· MUMBLE mumble ·:: MUMBLE·:·····D'YALL ····u·ti CLEARANCE REPEATED?

YEAH, CENTER — REPEAT ALL AFTER "IS CLEARED"!

LISSEN, ONE GOLF QUEBEC, Y'ALL GOT ENNY-BODY IN THAT AIRCRAFT WHO CAN SPEAK ENGLISH ?!

ROGER CENTER, WE DO! IF YOU'VE GOT ANYBODY DOWN THERE THAT DOES, PUT 'IM ON *and* WE'LL GET THIS CLEARANCE STRAIGHT-ENED OUT !!

The true story depicted on this page was told to me by a very disgruntled Piper pilot. You'll note that I've changed the brand names of the aircraft ever so slightly in most of these cartoons principally to avoid any lawsuits, the Belchcraft is a very thinly disguised reference to a Beechcraft and it doesn't take a lot of imagination to assume that the "Pooper Chickapee" could be a Piper Cherokee.

The teller of this story said that this situation actually occurred somewhere in the Northeast after a very tiring flight when tempers were a little frazzled. It isn't the recommended procedure for the proper flow of traffic. It can also result in your aircraft being sliced like a salami.

True story –

Just when I had commented that you would probably not see any more "Aviation Glossary" blurbs, up pops the devil. In this case, apparently I went back to using this method of depicting aviation humor as a gap filler.

The genesis of the chauffeur directing a pilot to his aircraft was a cartoon that I did many years ago for *Air Force* Magazine depicting how we Yanks viewed the RAF Eagle Squadron pilots back during the battle of Britain. We had been told that the pilots were provided with batmen and special niceties that went far beyond the pale of a normal combat pilot's realm. The original showed a picture of a chauffeur in a Rolls Royce directing his pilot, with a cup of tea in his hand, towards a Spitfire: "Only one mission today, sir?" The Brits loved it, but I received a few nasty letters from the Eagle Squadron.

The rest of the drawings are pretty routine, with the exception of the lower right, which actually happened. If you can visualize the landing light location on an aircraft, you can see how improbable this whole scenario is.

The little fellow in the tail dragger in the upper left-hand corner is real-
izing any small general aviation pilot's dream, i.e., having the heavy
iron wait. The basis for this cartoon was a trip that I made to a military
base in my little Mooney that held up—due to jet-wash conditions—a
C-5A, the biggest aircraft in the U.S. inventory. How sweet it was!

The waitress in the lower left-hand corner is pointing to a clown
that looks very much like the author. This particular idea actually
occurred in an airport near where I live and the waitress—needless to
say—was not there very long.

"WOULDN'T IT BE NICE -- FOR A CHANGE?"

CITABRIA 82 MIKE CLEARED FOR TAKE-OFF. GARGANTUAN FLIGHT 12 TAXI INTO POSITION & HOLD. CAUTION WAKE TURBULENCE DEPARTING CITABRIA.

AVIATION GLOSSARY

"MAKING A WINDS ALOFT REPORT"

HOW D'YA FIX AN ILS? HE SAYS HE JUST SHOT ONE and WANTS US TO COOK IT FOR HIS LUNCH.

MECHANICS - HERE'S HOW TO DRIVE A VAGUE PILOT TO THE FUNNY FARM:

| 3/10/80 | Something loose in tail. H. Rock, pilot |
| 3/11/80 | Something loose in tail has been tightened. |

Here we go again with communications. It just seems to crop up every time you start talking about flying. The pilot circling the airport was a lady who shall remain nameless. And the situation of the woman trying to find "point 7" on the ground actually happened to a couple of friends of mine at the Santa Barbara Airport in California.

"The computer battery is dead" stems from our current love affair with computerized things. I swear they'll have a "Computer of the Month Club" one of these days. Pilots are beginning to place an awful lot of importance upon what their computer tells them to do. This is both good and bad. When the computer dies, the pilot may follow suit. The old business of navigation by visual reference to the ground has all but been abandoned in some of our congested areas.

The lower right-hand corner is just another cheap shot at those poor overworked traffic controllers.

COMMUNICATIONS, OR THE LACK THEREOF:

EVER BEEN JUST A LITTLE BIT LOST? TRY THIS:

> UNKNOWN AIRPORT WITH A 150 CIRCLING OVERHEAD, IDENTIFY YOURSELF.

BREVITY IS NICE, BUT IT SURE CAN HONK UP THE WORKS FOR THE NOVICE(S)!

> THE TOWER SAID, "GO TO GROUND POINT 7". I CAN'T FIND **ANY** PLACE LIKE THAT ON THIS AIRPORT DIAGRAM— KEEP TAXIIN'...

WHAT WITH OUR DEPENDENCE ON THINGS ELECTRICAL ⸮

MAYDAY! MAYDAY

> MY COMPUTER'S BATTERY IS DEAD!

AND YOU KNOW HOW THEY TRAIN AIRCRAFT CONTROLLERS? THEY FILL THEIR MOUTHS WITH MARBLES *and* ...

LINCOLN'S GETTYSBURG ADDRESS

You must beat the second hand!

> ZPL PLP BFR PLP TXT BFF MUMPH BZT PLP ZT PSZFB UMPX PLP!

...WHEN THEY'VE LOST ALL THEIR MARBLES *and* YOU *STILL* CAN'T UNDERSTAND 'EM, THEY GRADUATE 'EM!

I started a series of cartoon pages called "Pet Peeves." This particular page is devoted to taxiing. There are almost as many funny anecdotes transmitted on the ground as while flying. To clarify things, the upper left-hand corner transmission was from another wiseacre pilot on the ramp.

The situation portrayed in the lower left-hand corner is right on. The Jeppesen mapmakers and the NOS (National Ocean Service) now print maps of all major airports, and by that I mean the biggies. These maps show the location number and direction of all taxiways. Without them you are completely lost.

PET PEEVES (TAXI DIV.)

HAVING ASKED FOR "TAXI INSTRUCTIONS" SOME CLOWN CUTS IN WITH —

FIRST, HOLD THE BRAKES FIRMLY; THEN, ADVANCE THE THROTTLE UNTIL YOU REACH 1200 RPM, THEN...

GETTING AN IFR CLEARANCE FROM A GRADUATE OF THE SCHOOL OF PHONETIC SANSKRIT —

Laeyo aoiou dxpo quto auoi bxyo mnstr. Bxhy cmbent dtnsti pxrnxo. Mnstr laeyo aoiou dxpo guto auoi bxgo. Pxrnxo bzny cmbent dtnsti. Bxyo mnstr laeyo aoiou dxop quto auoi. Dtnsti pxrnxo bzny cmbent. Avoi bxno mnstr laeyo aoiou dxpo quto. Cmbent dtnsti pxrnxo bzny. Quto avoi bxyo mnstr laeyo aoiou dxpo. Bzny cmbent dtnsti pxrnxo. Dxpo quto avoi bxyo mnstr laeyo aoiou. Pxrnxo bzny cmbent dtnsti. Aoiou dxpo quto avoi bxyo mnstr laeyo. Dtnsti pxrnxo cmbent. Laeyo aoiou dxpo quto avoi bxyo mnstr. Bzny cmbent dtnsti pxrnxo. Mnstr laeyo aoiou dxpo quto auoi bxyo. Pxrnxo bzny cmbnet dtnsti. Bxyo mnstr laeyo aoiou dxpo quto auoi. Stnsti pxrnxo bzny cmbent. Avoi bxno mnstr laeyo aoio dxpo quto. Dmbent dtnsti pxrnxó bzny. Quto avoi bxyo mnstr laeyo aoiou dxpo. Bzny cmbent dtnsti pxrnxo. Dxpo quto laeyo aoiu dxpo quto auoi bxyo mnstr. Bzny laeyo aoiou dxpo quto auoi bxyo mnstr. Bzny laeyo aoio dxpo quto auoi Laeyo aoiou quto auoi bxyo mnstr. Bxny cmbent dtnsti pxrnxo. Mnstr laeyo aoiou dxpo quto auoi bxgo.

AFTER BEING TOTALLY INTIMIDATED BY A BIG 'PORT'S TOWER, YOU ASK FOR "PROGRESSIVE INSTRUCTIONS" and...

ONE GOLF QUEBEC CLEARED TO EXECUTIVE VIA TAXIWAYS BRAVO TWO, ECHO ONE, DELTA FOUR and THE OUTER TO THE INNER OUTER VIA GOLF NINER. EXPEDITE!

QUICK! GIVE ME THE ROAD ATLAS!

201 GQ

THE RAMP "HELP" USED BY SOME OF THOSE BIG FBOs — NOTABLY IN TEXAS. (YOU *KNOW* I GOTTA BE KIDDIN' ON THIS ONE!)

ATION

PARK

DANGER

Bob Stevens

Continuing with "Pet Peeves." The situation depicted in the upper left-hand corner occurred to me at a civilian air base not far from my home and the place is well known for its pedantic tower operators. It doesn't do a thing towards helping pilot-controller relationships and there is certainly no place for lectures while you are in flight. End of sermon.

I don't believe I've been to any warm climate where the fuel tanks, when topped off, did not overflow upon releasing the caps. Of course you are supposed to release the cap to look at the color and amount of the fuel which has replaced the air in your tanks. Heat expansion in the wing will cause the tank to overflow, giving your shoes a distinct odor of avgas or Jet A. It's kind of a Catch-22. Your fuel-soaked shoes stay with you during the flight, of course, which causes passengers to stop smoking—not a bad idea at that.

On a sad note, the individual who pulled the stunt in the lower left-hand corner is no longer among the living. He did this just once too often. Unfortunately, he took another person with him.

Pet Peeves

YOU MAKE A MINOR COMM. BOO-BOO and THE TOWER GIVES YOU A LECTURE ON THE AIR TRAFFIC CONTROL SYSTEM—

YOU SAY, "TOP THE TANKS" and THE REFUELING TROOP FILLS 'EM 1¼ FULL—

THE CRETIN WHO MAKES AN UN-ANNOUNCED STRAIGHT-IN APPROACH.

THE HOT-SHOT WHO FIRES UP IN FRONT OF YOU ON THE DIRT and THEN THROWS MAX POWER TO IT!

The title, "You Know You're Getting To Be An Old Pilot When . . ." goes on for a couple of pages here. I don't know what got into me. I guess the fact that I had passed one of the biggies in my inexorable birthday march prompted me to reminisce about the days when a Ryan ST was the hottest thing going. I'd like to comment on the figure used throughout this page—it's yours truly. Ever since my graduation from flight school back in the U.S. Army Air Corps days, I've had the problem of what is known as "labile" high blood pressure: it goes up and down with mood swings. A nerd can set you off and it will go up without too much provocation. This problem started with an AAF (Army Air Forces) medical corpsman who announced to me after taking my blood pressure, "You'll never graduate and get your wings." (I had a slight rise in my blood pressure due to a case of German measles.) I have lived with "labile" for 35 years and have been looking for that corpsman ever since.

YOU *KNOW* YOU'RE GETTING TO BE AN OLD PILOT WHEN...

THE HOTTEST AIRPLANE YOU FLEW IN YOUR YOUTH IS DISPLAYED AS AN *ANTIQUE!*

SMART --- LINE KIDS START CALLING YOU "POPS" —

A TWO G TURN CAUSES SPOTS BEFORE YOUR EYES (AND YOU LOSE YOUR BIFOCALS) —

YOUR BLOOD PRESSURE AUTOMATICALLY GOES UP 20 PTS. AT THE *THOUGHT* OF A FLIGHT PHYSICAL —

The upper left-hand corner shows ol' dad trying to strain to see the instrument panel. It finally got so bad I had my bifocals cut so that I could read the instrument panel and also see long distances over the glare shield. I've heard it said that some of the older pilots flying the airlines have trifocals. They have the main instrument panel distance cut in the lower lens; the middle lens is cut for far distance; and the upper 1/8th, let's say, is for near, near distance. Then they can pop their head back and read the overhead panel.

The lower right-hand corner was an actual occurrence at a fly-in that pitted people of all levels of flying competence against one another. A gal with about 100 hours, I guess, beat ol' dad out by several hundred feet on the spot landing contest. The future belongs to the young.

...YOU NOTE THAT THEY'RE MAKING THE SEATS NARROWER 2nd MOVING THE INSTRUMENT PANEL FURTHER FORWARD!

...A LOOP REQUIRES 3 DAYS REMEDIAL ACTION WITH PREPARATION H!

AAARRGGH!

...THE INSTRUMENT INSTRUCTOR THEY ASSIGN YOU LOOKS YOUNGER'N YOUR TEENAGE SON!

SURF'S UP!

...YOU WATCH A SWEET YOUNG THING-WHO THINKS THE ADCOCK RANGE INCLUDES THE MOUNTAINS WEST OF EL PASO - ACE YOU OUT IN A SPOT LANDING CONTEST!

6000 + HRS

LOG

SQUEEK

Back to the "Pet Peeves" subject; in this case, the "urge to kill" department. Here again the reader will note that 75 percent of the page is
devoted to communications (and every one of them is true). The clod in
the lower right-hand corner is the one that gives people trying to land on
a single runway the most trouble. He's usually an instructor who has for-
gotten to tell his student something, and will start a lecture while in this
improbable position. This can back up traffic for several miles and raise
the blood pressure of those on final.

Pet Peeves
(OR THE URGE TO KILL)

1. HOW ABOUT THE CLOD WHO HORNS INTO THE NUMBER ONE POSITION and DOES HIS RUN-UP,...A *LONG* ONE?

2. YOU'RE LANDING AT A STRANGE FIELD IN A TOTALLY UNFAMILIAR AREA—

POOPER 16 SIERRA, YOU ARE CLEARED TO LAND—REPORT OVER GRANDMA'S BICYCLE SHOP...

3. AND HOW ABOUT THE NERD WHO MASHES DOWN ON THE MIKE BUTTON AN ICE AGE BEFORE ENGAGING HIS MIND?

4. THEN THERE'S THE JR. BIRDMAN WHO, WHEN GIVEN,"CLEARED FOR IMMEDIATE TAKEOFF," LAUNCHES INTO A THEORY OF FLIGHT LECTURE WITH HIS PASSENGER—

This page doesn't have a big message going for it except the story behind the wings with the screw emblazoned in the center. This idea prompted a special little project that we called ''Jest Wings:'' wings for various types of flying and flyers. They were cast from pewter and packaged in little boxes. We sold a whole bunch of them before tiring of the project. The instructor wings, I might add, were the most popular, followed closely by the Chairborne pilot, which was a picture of a chair with wings for those souls who had been ''kicked up the ladder.''

The cartoon in the lower right-hand corner was later used as a feature in *Private Pilot* Magazine called ''The Caption Contest.'' If you can imagine the balloon over the pilot's head being blank, we gave readers the chance to come up with the best caption they could imagine. I think the winning caption for this particular cartoon was (from the man watching below, saying in a thought bubble) ''Well, so much for the rubber-runway-and-concrete-tires idea.'' It just goes to show you how many good caption writers are out there.

TRAINING DAZE and FIRST SOLO

The "What's Worse Than . . .?" title came from another series done for a travel magazine many years ago and, by shifting gears, was simple to put it into the aviation field. But everything depicted is something that almost every pilot has experienced some time in his flying career.

The failure to close a flight plan has occurred to many of us; I was responsible for turning out the police one time for an overdue flight. In my case it was simply a matter of one of the semiannual time changes which caused the goof. Nonetheless, there's nothing quite as intimidating as seeing those people closing in on you. When the police finally got ahold of me, the officer queried his super by radio and said, "Well, what do we do now, give him a ticket?"

The lower two panels about flying through a TCA and VFR Corridor pertain almost exclusively to San Diego and Los Angeles and it *is* a hair-raising experience. The corridor was closed for a number of months recently and it created one *whale* of a problem!

WHAT'S WORSE THAN...?

This old gag came into popularity about the time hang gliders were at their zenith. You don't see too many hang gliders around any more because they've been banned from most controlled airspace areas. But the concept of the hippy flying the bird over a gun club brought many a laugh to people when it first appeared.

The hang glider future changed with power and now there are many makers of powered hang gliders, or as they are known in the trade, ultralights. These machines are proliferating at a fantastic clip and for a while it looked like they were going to take the place of the small general aviation aircraft. We wish them well because it is one of the few virtually unregulated methods of flying today.

"Coping with the fuel situation" is just one of several pages you'll see on this subject. The reader might recall that, when the first fuel crunch really hit the United States in the early '70s, it created chaos on the highways and skyways. The prices skyrocketed and Washington—in it's great wisdom—tried several techniques of coping with the situation, but none of them was quite successful. You just had to wait in long lines to get fuel in an automobile and in an aircraft sometimes you would find yourself at a field miles from nowhere with little or none of the brand that you normally burned. It got a little hairy.

In the lower right-hand corner, the Gossamer Condor, which appeared to me to be made of cellophane and *very* thin pieces of bamboo, made international news by flying a straight and then a circular course in the desert. Since this cartoon appeared, the Condor-type flights have crossed the English Channel and Aegean Sea and continue to set world records for manpowered flight. You've got to admit it would be one solution to the fuel shortage.

COPING WITH THE FUEL SITUATION

STEAM POWERED AIRCRAFT

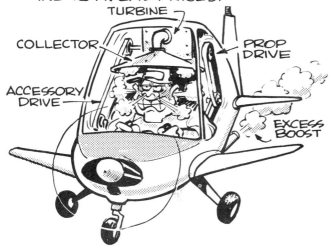

GASAHOL CONVER...

Here again is depicted the problems of congested air space and while it might seem a little calloused, the fellow in the upper left-hand corner is responding to his umpteenth call, no doubt, as to the location of traffic around him. The cartoon idea in the lower left-hand corner was given to me by the owner of a biplane—a beautiful bipe that had been *completely* restored. He swears it's a true story. Having left his helmet and goggles on the wingtip in the pre-flight process, he told his mechanic, who was flying with him, to go get them. The result took about six months to repair.

And just in case you hadn't noticed our Aviation Glossary is back with us again. I don't know how so many slipped by, but they all eventually ended up in the *Prop Wash* book. The E-6B shown here is practically archaic. What with modern hand-held computers, the E-6Bs might soon belong in the wing-warping era of flying.

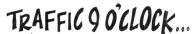
TRAFFIC 9 O'CLOCK...

HARRY! YOU PULLED THE GEAR UP TOO SOON! I THINK YOU GOT THE PROP. AREN'T WE GOING BACK TO CHECK FOR DAMAGE?

THE HELL WITH IT, LET 'EM FIX THEIR OWN RUNWAY!

NEVER MIND! I'LL GET 'EM!

AVIATION GLOSSARY

E6B: A DEVICE WHICH EXPLAINS WHY YOU WOULDN'T HAVE HAD ENOUGH FUEL TO GET THERE ANYWAY.

SPUT   WHEEZ!

COUGH!

All of the cartoons here are self-explanatory—as any good cartoon should be—however, I would like to comment on the lower three sequences. This particular gag came to me from a friend who worked in the air traffic control business and is probably one of the funniest gags that a person can tell in front of an audience. I have spent many years speaking before large groups of aviation-oriented people and this one particular gag has always been a "*gotcha!*" As in all good comic routines, the punch line is the one that makes it or breaks it.

I believe the term "say again" is used more in the air than any other phrase on this planet. The Air Force Academy's publication, *The Talon*, had a magnificent article on "Good Communications is Never Having to Say Huh?" Very true.

The gag about landing across the runway came to me from an actual experience in British Columbia where bush pilots often land on very short runways and in heavy timber. They are quite adept at what they do . . . the challenge posed by this tower operator was just too much to be ignored.

I hope no one is offended by the ersatz Japanese in the lower panels. There are many foreign students training in the U.S. because of the dollar rate of exchange. Most of the pilots have been coming from Japan. To listen to them merely describe their pattern position strains the ol' eardrums.

SAY AGAIN ?

NINETY PERCENT OF AVIATION HUMOR IS COMMUNICATIONS - OR THE LACK THEREOF. WE PRESENT HEREWITH SOME CLASSIC EXAMPLES OF THE LATTER. NO OFFENSE IS INTENDED TOWARD THE NATIONALITIES INVOLVED - THIS IS JUST THE WAY IT **IS** -

WE'VE *ALL* HEARD THE ETHNIC JOKE ABOUT THE SHORT, WIDE RUNWAY... FROM CANADA COMES THIS TALE ABOUT A TOWER OPERATOR WHO - FOR TRAFFIC FLOW - WANTED A BIRD TO LAND ON THE <u>OTHER</u> SIDE OF A RUNWAY BISECTING THE ACTIVE -

AIRCRAWFT ON FINAL, LAND ACROSS RUNWAY 8 !

HEH, HEH. I'LL BET THAT'S THE LAST TIME HE SAYS THAT TO A STOL.

THERE ARE A LOT OF FOREIGN STUDENTS TRAINING IN THE U.S. THESE DAYS, ESPECIALLY GERMAN *and* JAPANESE. THE LANGUAGE BARRIER IS FORMIDABLE, PARTICULARLY FOR THE ASIAN STUDENTS -

RIN BERG TOWAH THIS NUMBAH TLEE LEVEN RIMA. REFT CLOSSWISE REG. RANDING LUNWAY TLEE SRIX.

AIRCRAFT THAT JUST CALLED, SAY AGAIN.

AFTER TWO OR THREE EXCHANGES LIKE THIS, THE EXASPERATED TOWER OPERATOR LETS FLY WITH -

AIRCRAFT CALLING LIMBERG TOWER, GIVE ME YOUR MESSAGE IN PHONETICS !!

VELLY SORRY - NO SPEAK FONETIC. OKAY IN JAPANESE ?

We deal with a very delicate subject here—the biological need to relieve oneself from time to time while flying.

The incident depicted in the lower left-hand corner was a system we used in the military (only at times of great duress!). We were flying light air support aircraft at high altitudes in the winter. These planes were sans "facilities." When on instruments it became almost suicidal to execute a letdown over mountainous terrain in order to perform the necessary biological functions before pressing on. So we devised a system of using condoms (that used to be a dirty word in the publishing world, but now with all the ads regarding a certain sociological disease, it's no longer taboo). These make great reservoirs for liquid. You can imagine the velocity and consistency of such a "balloon" dropped from 10,000 or 12,000 feet through freezing rain! We sincerely hoped that no one below us ever received such a missle. To my knowledge a direct hit has never been reported.

"WHEN YOU GOTTA GO, YOU GOTTA..."

A DELICATE SUBJECT, BUT ONE THAT IS NEAR *and* DEAR TO THE HEARTS (BLADDERS?) OF ALL WHO FLY GENERAL AVIATION BIRDS SANS "FACILITIES"—

ALL KINDS OF UNORTHODOX CONTAINERS HAVE BEEN PRESSED INTO SERVICE.* IT'S DISPOSAL ONCE ON THE GROUND THAT BECOMES A PROBLEM.

* ONE DISTRAUGHT FEMALE PASSENGER HAD TO USE HER GUCCI HANDBAG!

THEN THERE WAS THE LADY WHO CLIMBED INTO THE BACK SEAT *and* DREW THE CURTAINS (IN CASE OF A PASSING AIRLINER)

DON'T TRY THE AIRDROP SYSTEM !! CAN YOU IMAGINE THE TERMINAL VELOCITY OF A 2 LB BALLOON OF LIQUID JETTISONED @ 10,000 FT. WITH THE TEMP. AT, SAY, MINUS 10°C ?!

DON'T BE MISLED INTO BELIEVING THAT THE AMOUNT YOU DRINK IN FLIGHT OUT OF ANY GIVEN CONTAINER WILL RE-OCCUPY THE SAME SPACE.*

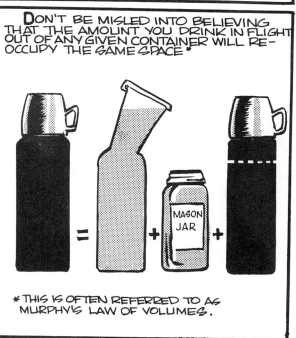

* THIS IS OFTEN REFERRED TO AS MURPHY'S LAW OF VOLUMES.

There's not a whole lot to be said for this page, except that it uses visual images rather than the written word to tell the stories.

Regarding the upper right-hand corner, I saw a cartoon in *Ag Pilot* Magazine that was very similar to this particular drawing. I was impressed with its clarity and tried to make a ''legitimate switch'' (of the idea). That cost me the free subscription I had. After that, things kind of fell apart in my association with the publisher. Anyway, my general theme for drawing does not include crop dusting, so there was no great loss.

SIGN LANGUAGE

FOR STUDENTS

FOR CROPDUSTERS

FOR FAA EXAM ROOMS

FOR SHORT FIELDS

I used to eat at an airport cafe nearby, and, while waiting for my cold hamburger to arrive, observed the various types of flying individuals that came and went. The characters shown here are accurate. As a matter of fact, I once saw a solo student try to make a sandwich out of one of his private pilot manuals, he was so engrossed in reading another manual lying nearby.

And, of course, I had to take a shot at the FAA examiner with his write-up. This was done many years ago, before the "tightening up" of regulation enforcement—it proved to be very prophetic.

AIRPORT CAFE CHARACTERS

OLD WARRIOR

HEAVY-IRON JOCK

SOLO STUDENT

FAA EXAMINER

An Oregon company suggested audible signal devices for aircraft—yes, that means horns. This item was labeled "news" and ran in a popular aviation magazine. This idea struck me as being one of the most ludicrous things that could possibly be used on aircraft, unless, of course, it was of such size and had the power to pop rivets at 15 miles.

I went right off the wall in depicting how these horns—should they be produced—would be used in various types of air machines. There's no question that the Fed's siren would be appropriate. The point is, where would the guy pull over to? If the 747 with the steamboat whistle didn't force the aircraft out of the way with its volumetric efficiency, it would probably zap the bird into a zillion pieces by sound waves alone. Of course, the blast could incapacitate the pilot. In any event, the aircraft would soon disappear from the flight path of the horn-carrying vehicle.

Maybe they should rethink this one.

(NEWS ITEM) AN OREGON COMPANY HAS SUGGESTED AUDIBLE SIGNAL DEVICES, *e.g.* AIRCRAFT **HORNS**, AS A MEANS OF COLLISION AVOIDANCE. CONSIDER THE POSSIBILITIES!

TRAINERS

ANTIQUES

THE FEDS

HEAVY IRON

All pilots and plane owners, by virtue of their records stashed away in Oklahoma City's archives, fall victim to a huge volume of mail order aviation "wish books." These catalogs are detailed and in living color now. Virtually every page yields something that you "just *have* to have."

On this particular page, I took the norm and went a few steps forward to make it ridiculous. The whole catalog thing can be summed up by the guy in the lower right-hand panel who bought so much stuff that he couldn't get into the airplane to fly, thereby making it the ultimate flight safety machine.

I swear that someday they will have a "gadget of the month" club, which will enable wish book devotees to send in and get the gimmick of the month. There seem to be more gadget makers out there than there are pilots.

THE SUBJECT IS PILOT SUPPLY "WISH BOOKS." SOME OF THE OFFERINGS ARE PRETTY SOPHISTICATED. IF YOU BUY, CAVEAT EMPTOR. IN ANY CASE - *READ THE INSTRUCTIONS*

The aviation doodles idea shown here came from a book done many years ago by Roger Price. Roger was tops in his field of drawing clever line drawings.

His book *Droodles* was published by Price/Stern/Sloan Publishers Inc. in Los Angeles many years ago. He also appeared on national TV. One of his funniest routines was illustrating "the T zone"—an ad theme used by a big cigarette maker.

If I had his imagination and talent, perhaps there would be a book of aviation doodles instead of the stuff you're now reading.

AVIATION DOODLES

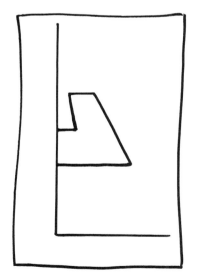

1. INVERTED LAPSE RATE
2. MOONEY IN SHORT HANGAR.

1. HORIZON AS SEEN BY PILOT WITH VERTIGO.
2. _____
(YOUR CAPTION)

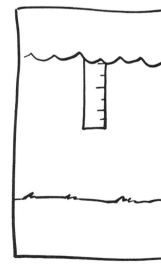

1. HELICOPTER MAKING A PRECISION APPROACH.
2. CLOUD WITH ITS OWN RAIN GAUGE.

I have no idea about the genesis of the idea on the page opposite. It just seemed to me that there are sufficient off-the-wall screwballs flying around that this type of individual pilot *could* exist.

I know that in drawing No. 4 the expression ''Phew! Cheated death again!'' was used by us in the military quite often when flying with another military pilot or passenger. Maybe I just backed into that idea and created the other three pictures to match. In any event, just one of the statements used on the page by a pilot is grounds for a justifiable homicide on the part of the passenger(s).

Snappy sayings to keep your passengers amused and alert—

1. After engine start:

2. Just prior to takeoff:

3. During takeoff roll:

4. On shutdown:

The top half of this page, "Special Equipment for Pilots," was given to me by Paul Stebelton. Paul was an accident prevention type in the FAA, working out of Long Beach, California. Paul went around giving lectures on how to avoid pranging an airplane. He is a fine man and gave excellent attention-grabber type talks. Paul was so dedicated to safety that when it came to a showdown on what he felt was wrong about some of the policies used by the growing bellicosity of the FAA, he resigned his position rather than knuckle under. That takes guts.

The TLAR is a gimmick that came out of the Vietnam unpleasantness and was a gag said to have been used by light plane pilots in marking targets. If you believe this story, I have a bridge to sell you.

I think the flying glasses for hydrophobic pilots came from a conversation with Paul over a bottle of soda pop.

SPECIAL EQUIPMENT FOR PILOTS
(PATS. PENDING)

THE EMERGENCY ALL WEATHER INSTRUMENT FLYING HELMET

CAN
'WINDOW'
CANDLE
BRACE
FLY SAFE
HARD HAT

WHAT'S THE WORST SITUATION THAT FACES AN INSTRUMENT-RATED PILOT? *Ans:* **COMPLETE ELECTRICAL** *and* **VACUUM FAILURE AT NIGHT IN WEATHER, THAT'S WHAT!**

HOW IT WORKS:
IN DIVE, MORE OF CAN APPEARS —

CANDLE ILLUMINATES PANEL, WHICH BUILDS CONFIDENCE IN THE COCKPIT.

IN CLIMB, LESS OF CAN IS IN VIEW —

NOTE! CAN HITTING BRACE GIVES AUDIBLE STALL WARNING!

FLY THE CAN!
BOTTOM OF THE CAN AS SEEN BY THE WEARER:

HELMET

GONE!

STRAIGHT & LEVEL   LEFT BANK   RIGHT BANK   UPSIDE DOWN!

IN THIS SITUATION, THE HARD HAT IS USEFUL FOR TERMINATION OF FLIGHT.

"DON'T DROP THE AIRPLANE TO FLY THE MICROPHONE!"

THE **TLAR** (**T**HAT **L**OOKS **A**BOUT **R**IGHT) THUMB-MOUNTED VASI

REMOVES ALL DOUBT ABOUT THOSE CUTE VASI SAYINGS e.g. "RED OVER RED, YOU'RE DEAD" etc.

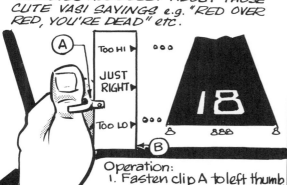

(A)
TOO HI ► ooo
JUST RIGHT ►
18
TOO LO ► ooo
(B) ◄

Operation:
1. Fasten clip A to left thumb.
2. Hold out and align top mark with most distant VASI lights.
3. Determine approach angle on card B.

FLYING GLASSES FOR THE PILOT WHO HATES FLYING OVER WATER—

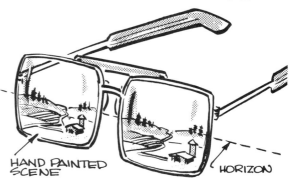

HAND PAINTED SCENE

HORIZON

- PLAIN GLASS OR PRESCRIPTION
- CLEAR OR ROSE TINTED
- CHOICE OF GROUND SCENES—URBAN OR RURAL
- WILL FLOAT

The airport depicted on the opposite page came from the fertile mind of a pilot in Carlsbad, California. Local citizens in the flight pattern of Palomar Airport have very successfully campaigned against a parallel runway for expansion of the airport. His solution, graphically portrayed here, has its shortcomings, but what the hey, you'll never know unless you try it!

The forces aligned against Palomar Airport are still active in their condemnation proceedings. It's painful to say, but this type of activity by local uninformed citizens is resulting in fewer and fewer airports in our country.

The lower part of the page covers a supposedly true exchange between L.A. Center—which gets *very* busy—and a certain local flying physician. The doc had a large mouth, small mind, and a tendency to use both. He never took time to get an instrument rating and therefore was the bane of every controller in that sector when the weather got marginal.

EXPANSION OF EXISTING GENERAL AVIATION AIRPORTS TO HANDLE MORE TRAFFIC IS NIGH ON TO IMPOSSIBLE WHAT WITH PRIVATE INTEREST, "ANTI-EVERTHING" and ENVIRONMENTAL GROUPS. HERE'S A SOLUTION FOR DOUBLING RUNWAY CAPABILITY:

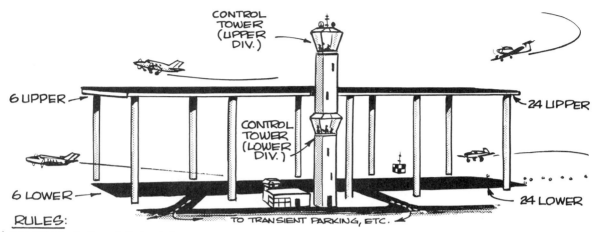

RULES:

1. TOUCH and GOES ON UPPER **ONLY**.
2. STRAIGHT-OUTS ON LOWER **ONLY**.
3. RIGHT TRAFFIC PATTERN UPPER.
4. LEFT   "   "   LOWER.
5. IFR APPROACH -**PRECISION**- ON LOWER.
6. ALL TRANSIENTS LAND ON LOWER, PLS!
7. NO "WITH THE OPTION" ON EITHER.
8. NO GO-AROUNDS ON LOWER.

HEAR THE ONE ABOUT THE PHYSICIAN-PILOT WHO WAS ALWAYS BADMOUTHING CONTROLLERS BOTH ON and OFF THE AIR? ONE DARK and STORMY NIGHT THE CHICKENS CAME HOME TO ROOST—

The series of "Why is it . . . ?" appeared in a magazine that I worked for. We picked these situations as the ones most pilots seemed to encounter. The phrase "Fallbrick Air Park" refers to our hometown airport for a number of years (Fallbrook, California). The runway is short (I think they gratuitously call it 2000 feet; actually, there's about 1800 feet usable). Pilots become very proficient in short field landings here. Once in a while a bird will mush off into the avocado trees for a short distance. On the other hand, many heavy iron birds have managed Fallbrook with a great deal of finesse.

We flew for a while in the great "Northwet." Pictures like the lower right-hand corner filled our windshield on more than one occasion in the area between Seattle and the Canadian border. It's something you just have to get used to.

WHY IS IT...?

...UNFAMILIAR RURAL FIELDS LOOK LIKE SOMETHING YOU BUY AT THE POST OFFICE?

...RUNWAYS ON A HILL ALWAYS LOOK LIKE YOU'RE APPROACHING THE ENTERPRISE?

...LANDING AT A BIG METRO 'PORT MAKES YOU FEEL LIKE YOU'VE TOUCHED DOWN IN THE MIDDLE OF THE BONNEVILLE SALT FLATS?

..., RUNWAYS IN MOUNTAINOUS TERRIAN ALWAYS SEEM TO BE SET IN A NATIONAL FOREST?

This is a true story. It happened to yours truly. I needed a new clock for my instrument panel and the financial strings of the old family budget were stretched pretty tight. I figured I could do it myself. Well, it took about a day-and-a-half to do what is compressed into three drawings here. Of course, I fouled up more things than I fixed. I can't remember what the final bill was, but it was in orbit. They had to replace major components in the back of the panel, plus some electrical fuses that were located near the battery (those I blew out at the very beginning of the project). There's a lesson in here somewhere.

A tearsheet of this cartoon hangs on the wall of the shop where I had the damage repaired. The owner shows it to any customer who utters the classic phrase, "Hell, I can fix it myself!"

NASA has a neat publication entitled *Callback*, which is produced at the Naval Air Station, Moffatt Field, California. Pilots can report with impunity to this Aviation Safety Reporting System any near-misses or other boo-boos. Some of the stories that pilots have related through Callback, which is distributed to all subscribers free, are truly amazing; these are two such stories.

The situation shown in the lower right-hand corner has been duplicated many, many times in military flying. Usually it is the result of a breakdown in communication (heard that one before?). This actually happened to me way back in 1942 in primary flight school while flying a PT-22. We recovered at something approximating the height of July corn.

"GOOD COMMUNICATION IS NEVER HAVING TO SAY, 'HUH'?"

TRUE STORY—

...and AFTER A VERY FEW MINUTES—

It might seem to the reader that I take many unnecessary shots at controllers and the FAA bureaucracy, but you'll have to admit that they make a pretty big target! In any event, there are many cases on record where controllers—locked in their little dark rooms far below us—have saved the lives of pilots and passengers through their cool thinking.

I'd like to go on record here; I applaud the work they do!

The lower right-hand corner dates this piece of work. It was obviously drawn about the time we had the Olympics in Los Angeles. It was the summer of 1984 and many gags regarding the Olympic grading system came out in all walks of life. This one seemed particularly appropriate because of its relationship to the high jump and other track events.

It had to happen sooner or later. Murphy's Law, as we all know, describes those situations where everything is fouled up and there is no one else to blame it on except poor old Murph. The source of this information I erroneously gave as the University of Nebraska which had reprinted the material in their monthly aviation publication. Come to find out, there were at least two other references and/or originators of Murphy's Law applied to aviation—one of them being Mr. Jim Weir, of Radio Systems Engineering and the other a fellow by the name of Klipstein. Klipstein was an electronics engineer and the source of his material goes back to 1967.

Taking all of this written material and transposing it into graphic form was a fun project. I had seen some of these things happen to pilots and mechanics. I was the subject of several minor catastrophes myself. I've never been very good at things mechanical, and when it comes to performing maintenance, that's ol' dad in the last scene.

HOME BASE WILL ALWAYS BE 5 MIN. BEYOND THE MAX RANGE OF YOUR BIRD AT LAST PLANNED STOP.

WINDS ALOFT REPORTS WILL ONLY BE ACCURATE IN THE CASE OF DIRECT HEADWINDS.

ANSWERS ON FAA EXAMS WILL BE EQUIDISTANT FROM YOUR COMPUTED ANSWER(S).

ON OVERWATER FLIGHTS, THE ENGINE WILL GO INTO AUTO ROUGH AT MIDPOINT + OR - 10 MIN.

IN PERFORMING MAINTENANCE, AFTER AN INSPECTION PLATE WITH 26 SCREWS HAS BEEN REMOVED, IT WILL PROVE TO BE THE WRONG PLATE.

AFTER 26 SCREWS HAVE BEEN REPLACED IN THE INSPECTION PLATE, THE GASKET WILL BE FOUND ON THE WORK BENCH.

Continuing with Murphy's Law, we have a combination of both pilotage and mechanical happenstances. The actual credits for these particular ideas are given at the bottom of the page.

I have no idea what Edsel Murphy would look like as a pilot, but I drew him in the upper right-hand corner as a guy who could never quite make things come together. Naturally he'd have to be wearing a ''Win'' badge that was used in Jerry Ford's ''Whip Inflation Now'' campaign. As far as coordination is concerned, Jerry Ford cannot be compared to, say, Rudolph Nureyev.

THE PREVIOUS PAGE WE DEPICTED "MURPHY'S LAW APPLIED TO AVIATION". LET US MEET THE MAN → and EXAMINE HIS LAW FURTHER. HIS PROFOUND CONCEPTS OF THE 20TH CENTURY ARE DESTINED FOR A SECURE PLACE IN THE AVIATION HALL OF FAME. HIS LAW - THOUGH INHERENTLY SIMPLE - HAS FORMED A FOUNDATION ON WHICH FUTURE GENERATIONS WILL BUILD.[1] HERE, THEN, IS MURPHY'S **BASIC** LAW:

$$1 + 1 \; \rightarrow \; 2$$

(WHERE ☞ IS THE SYMBOL FOR "HARDLY EVER"[2].)

EDSEL MURPHY

MURPHY'S LAW APPLIED TO AVIATION MANUALS and MAINTENANCE PT II

"Operating manuals will express dimensions in the least usable form. e.g. velocity will be expressed in furlongs per fortnight & fuel consumption in hogsheads per gigasecond[1]."

CLINK! CLANG! GLUNK!

OH ----!

..."a dropped tool will hit a spot where it will do maximum damage (Murphy's law of selective gravitation)."

"The component most likely to fail will be the least accessible."

FZZZ ZAP!

"A failsafe circuit will not only fail, it will destroy others as it does so."

REFERENCES :
1. JIM WEIR, EEE, RADIO SYS. ENG. " THE CONTRIBUTIONS OF EDSEL MURPHY TO THE ART and SCIENCE OF FLYING"
2. " THE CONTRIBUTIONS OF EDSEL MURPHY TO THE UNDERSTANDING OF BEHAVIOR OF INANIMATE OBJECTS " KLIPSTEIN, EEE, AUG 1967 pp 91-92.

Here's a little bit of that jugular vein humor we mentioned in the Fore-word of the book. It's not particularly funny, however, most pilots have experienced *some* of the situations shown here.

The last drawing on the page is *definitely* a jugular vein cartoon. I used it once for a political cartoon showing what would happen to some Labor Day drivers who got drunk, were in a hurry, etc. The paper received several letters condemning me for the black approach to this subject. However, I received not one beef from pilots when this ap-peared—it is such a truism.

FAMOUS LAST WORDS

This is a page done by a man who was desperate for material. After sitting at the drawing board for about two hours and having nothing come to mind, it occurred to me to start thumbing through material that had piled up in the studio. I found a list of the phobias in the *World Book Encyclopedia*. By delving a little further, I found that the University of Chicago, Office of the Medical Center and Public Affairs, had produced a long list of the various mental aberrations that affect people in all walks of life.

I picked out six of the ones that I thought were most appropriate for birdmen, and that's what you see here. The thing you don't see here is that when I signed this page in its final form I signed it as "Bob Stevens, a sufferer of ergasiophobia—one who has a morbid aversion to work."

EVER WONDER WHY YOUR PALMS SWEAT (male) OR PERSPIRE (fem.) DURING EXAMS, FLIGHT CHECKS, etc.? HERE ARE THE <u>OFFICIAL</u> PHOBIAS WHICH AFFECT FLYERS:

ACROPHOBIA - FEAR OF HIGH PLACES. AN OLDIE; FIRST SUFFERED BY ICARUS FLYING AEGEAN V-22.

GEE! I WISH DAD HAD WORKED ON PARACHUTES, INSTEAD!

AGORAPHOBIA - FEAR OF CROSSING, OR BEING IN LARGE, OPEN SPACES. CAN BE TRACED TO EARLY TRANS-OCEANIC FLTS.

WHAT THE H___ AM I DOING OUT HERE?!

BATOPHOBIA - FEAR OF PASSING NEAR OR AMONG HIGH OBJECTS. EPIDEMIC AMONG WWII PILOTS FLYING THE HIMALAYAS.

IF I EVER GET OUT OF THIS ALIVE, I'M GONNA BE A CROP DUSTER!

BRONTOPHOBIA (NO, IT'S *NOT* FEAR OF MEETING A BRONTOSAURUS) - IT'S FEAR OF THUNDERSTORMS

DON'T WORRY, FOLKS. IT'S A PERFECTLY *NORMAL* PHOBIA!

MYTHOPHOBIA - FEAR OF MAKING FALSE STATEMENTS. RARE AMONG PILOTS WITH ONE NOTEABLE EXCEPTION-

PHOTOPHOBIA - FEAR OF FEAR. NO KIDDIN' - MAKE UP YOUR OWN!

NIGHT, IFR, OUTTA GAS, LOST, MTS. LESSEE, HOW DID F.D.R. PUT IT? "THE ONLY THING WE HAVE TO FEAR IS FEAR ITSELF"

This is an actual experience that I had with my Mooney 201. The Mooney is a marvelous machine and I loved every moment I had it. Well, there were a few occasions. In this particular instance I was having trouble with my altitude hold in the autopilot system. I went to my good friend Rick Otto, of Otto Instruments in Ontario, California, to have the work done. One of the best autopilot repairmen in the business was put on the job immediately and it was fixed in short order.

You'll note the Otto insignia in the building on the lower panel and a caricature of the owner. I do this from time to time with people I know very well. A college student punched me in the eye for a demeaning caricature I had done of him in the school paper—learning taboos comes, early in this business.

Again, the action depicted here happened at an airport near our home at a place called Rancho California. Of course, I had to hokey around with the name and change it to "Roncho," but anyone in these parts knows that the crosswinds can be horrendous here in the afternoon on a sunny, hot day.

This basic idea came from a book I did many years ago in the recreational vehicle business where a neophyte tried to hook up an RV the first time out and, of course, had it all backwards. This just proves, I guess, that the basis of humor can take many different forms.

As any pilot of a fuel-injected aircraft knows, there are myriad ways to start a hot engine. The blasted little devils, when they get hot, seem to have a mind all their own. No one procedure seems to work every time. I have shown three of the basic methods to use, which, on occasion, have started the little IO-360 engine in the Mooney.

I wouldn't say that the best procedure is uncomplicated, however, when trying to demonstrate it to a fellow Mooney pilot one day—as his hands flew through the ritual required to move certain levers very rapidly—he took about a quarter of an inch of skin off his knuckle and said, "Well, that's enough of *that* kind of starting."

Waiting for the engine to cool in a tightly cowled bird can take all day, so bring your lunch.

HOT STARTS

SOME AIRCRAFT ENGINES ARE NOTORIOUSLY HARD TO HOT START. THERE SEEM TO BE AS MANY PROCEDURES AS PILOTS. WE PRESENT HEREWITH THOSE TECHNIQUES WHICH HAVE PROVEN SURE-FIRE (pardon the pun. ed.) AS TAKEN FROM THE YET-TO-BE-PUBLISHED "HOT START OF THE MONTH" CLUB NEWS.

1
 a. Flood the engine.
 b. Use "flood start" procedure.
 c. Have fire truck handy.

2
 a. Grind away on starter until battery is dead.
 b. Replace battery.
 c. Repeat a. above.

3
 a. Crank with everything "off"
 b. Move mixture & throttle forward together.
 c. Retard throttle & advance mixture while continuing to crank and prime.
 d. If engine fires, let person providing 3rd and 4th hands go.

4 If all else fails, wait until engine cools and use normal start.

Every pilot who's thought about buying a new piece of equipment for his aircraft, and is married, will commiserate with the guy in the upper left-hand corner. In my own situation, every time a new piece of equipment was added to the bird, the wife added something to her own personal wardrobe. This "tit-for-tat" business permeates the general aviation field.

To diverge a minute, I know a friend who collects guns—real *big* guns. His latest acquisition is a French 75 field piece. You can imagine the size of the ring that his wife got out of that cannon. I believe the diameter of the stone was something on the order of 75mm.

Here again we see the divergence of opinions on how to start a fuel-injected engine, a well-worn subject in our field. And then, to cap off the page, "You Know It's Going to be a Rotten Day When . . ." was kind of an afterthought. Later you will see that we made a whole series out of this subject.

After forty some years of drawing aviation cartoons, I think I've run into just about every type of editor there is in the business. For years I tried to ram the acid rain cartoon past a particular editor. This man had a complete aversion to showing an aircraft in *any* damaged condition. Finally, out of desperation, I threw it at Dennis Shattuck at *Private Pilot* and it went by without a hitch.

The bottom half of the page takes another shot at ATC and in this particular instance I was told that the story is true. The boys in the L.A. Center can become pretty testy at times and one can hardly blame them since they handle thousands of blips on their radar screens every day. Many of these blips are converging. I don't think I'd last a day on the scope. The transmission out of the blue, or in this case, the muck, was obviously from some other pilot who had tangled with center controllers earlier.

Every once in a while a cartoonist has to get cute. The "play the aviation word game" is a prime example. Some of the words are so obvious that they don't need to be illustrated; however, there are a couple that are rather obscure. The whole point of this thing is that the so-called quiz is a little different from the ordinary cartoon fare and, besides, I never got a nasty letter drawing this subject.

Active pilots are rarely stay-at-home guys. Some of them use any excuse to go out to the airport and hangar fly, bum a ride, or just rest. I have one friend who spends every day of his week going out to the local FBO and hangar flying with the locals and drop-ins. It's great therapy and it keeps him from all those little "honey do" chores at home.

PLAY THE AVIATION WORD GAME!! (answers below)

a. TOUGH TO LAND IN:

b. YOU DO IT BEFORE TAKEOFF:

c. HARD ON BRAKES and TIRES:

→ FIELD ←

d. WEATHER CONDITION:

↓ C E I L I N G ↓

e. SOMETHING YOU SEE AT AIR SHOWS:

ANSWERS: a. CROSS WIND   b. MAG CHECK c. SHORT FIELD   d. LOW CEILING   e. FLY BYE   (g. WAN, TRY SOME YOURSELF!)

GREAT GREETINGS

Here's that "It never fails" subject again. I believe there's nearly a full book of these drawings. In this particular case I was reminded of my military flying days when getting strapped into a pressurized high-speed jet fighter required much physical exertion, just the "trigger" needed for the biological urge to strike.

To remedy the situation shown here, I began to carry along a H.E.R.E. bottle made out of plastic. It saw a lot of service in my flying career. (The initials stand for Human Endurance Range Extender.)

" IT NEVER FAILS..."

YOU COMPLETE AN EXHAUSTIVE PREFLIGHT,...

GET ALL YOUR COMMUNICATION GEAR ADJUSTED JUST RIGHT...

SOMEONE'S BEEN MESSIN' WITH THIS HEADSET AGIN

STRAP YOURSELF IN and ARRANGE YOUR CHARTS FOR READY REFERENCE...

GAD! THERE'S 4 UNFILED REVISIONS

TWANG!

STUDY THE DEPARTURE PLATE and CLIP IT IN PLACE...

LESSEE, RUNWAY HEADING TO 3000, THEN...

CALL CLEARANCE DELIVERY and GIVE 'EM ALL THE VITALS...

...READY TO COPY.

THEN *IT* STRIKES!

I'VE GOTTA GO TO THE JOHN!

"The Urge To Kill Department" could just as well have been labeled "It Never Fails." I was on that kind of a roll when I drew this cartoon and the one on the preceding page. Solo instrument flying is a pretty demanding task even under the best of situations; to have a clearance cancelled or amended after becoming airborne comes very close to panic-button-pushing-time.

The ersatz German nomenclature used here had its genesis in a book that I described earlier: *Prop Wash*. This little book sold a lot of copies in Europe. The section dealing with the Germans has been widely reprinted throughout the GAF (German Air Force). Contrary to the West's impression of the stern Prussian soldier, the new Germans can laugh at themselves.

THE-URGE-TO-KILL DEPT.

ATC GIVES YOU A COMPLICATED CLEARANCE BEFITTING A 747 FLIGHT TO NOME- REPLETE WITH SID, LIMITS, HOLDS, ETC...

YOU *FINALLY* GET THE PLATE IN PLACE, YOUR SQUAWK CODE, RELEASE TIME, VECTOR TO YOUR FIRST FIX and BLAST OFF...

JUST AS YOU ENTER THE SOUP THE CONTROLLER COMES UP WITH THIS GEM...

AT LAST!

POOPER 42 ECHO CANCEL YOUR ORIGINAL CLEARANCE. I HAVE AN AMENDMENT. ARE YOU READY TO COPY?

EVER WONDER WHAT OUR ILLUSTRATED AVIATION GLOSSARY WOULD LOOK LIKE IN, SAY, GERMAN - *FRACTURED GERMAN*? ENJOY.

DER FLIEGENWAGEN— (EIN DREIPOINTER GROUNDEN- LOOPER FLIEGENWAGEN)

DER SCHWEINHUND SCHTUCK MIT DER DUMKOPFT LERNEN FLIEGEN

DAS IST DER DUMKOPFT LERNEN FLIEGEN

DER GROUNDENBOUNCER FLIEGENWAGEN MIT GE- TRAINEN VHEEL

DER UPPENDOWNER SCHTICKS MIT ROUNDENROLLERS.

DER OFFROARENBAHNSTRASSE

Here's more of the "You Know It's Going To Be a Rotten Day When . . ." material. The only surprise on this particular page is the lower right-hand cartoon.

I have been called a male chauvinist pig by some ladies in the aviation business. Several of my cartoons depicting the distaff element have drawn an awful lot of flak. I was really braced for trouble when I did the one on this page. Much to my surprise, one of the most revered flying grandmothers in the business came up to me and said this was the funniest cartoon she had ever seen. I felt somehow vindicated at that point, and started using women in my drawings again.

YOU *KNOW* IT'S GOING TO BE A ROTTEN DAY WHEN—

...YOU CUT THE CORNER OF A RESTRICTED AREA HOMEWARD BOUND, WALK IN and...

...THE GUY YOU ACED OUT OF THE LAST PARKING SPOT IN THE LOT TURNS OUT TO BE THE FLIGHT EXAMINER ABOUT TO GIVE YOU A CHECK RIDE—

...YOU'RE BARELY AIRBORNE IN YOUR NEWLY-UPHOLSTERED PRIDE and JOY WHEN THE PASSENGER YELLS, "QUICK! WHERE'S THE SICK SACK?"

...YOU SUDDENLY REMEMBER YOU FORGOT TO CLOSE YOUR FLIGHT PLAN—

Continuing with the same subject as the preceding page, I can recall several of these cartoons vividly because they were traumas in my life. The arrival of the mail had a particular terror for me during a period of FAA crackdown on maintenance procedures of the particular airplane I owned. It seemed that every other delivery brought one of those damnable ADs (airworthiness directives) and, as anybody knows, an AD usually results in a large outlay of cash before your plane can become airborne again. The ADs on this particular bird—which shall remain nameless—became so numerous that I eventually sold it off. We were lucky; we had only taken an eight grand bath.

The instructor giving the student stall instruction again goes back to military experience. This gag stemmed from flying a T-33 jet trainer. The old T-Bird, as she was known, was a grand and mostly forgiving lady. Like all fixed-wing birds, it would absolutely refuse to fly at zero airspeed. In the T-Bird you could pull her straight up and hold the stick back until you saw zero on the indicator, at which time she would swap ends and point straight down until speed had built up to the point where it would pull itself out and repeat the process. I never tried more than two of these maneuvers consecutively because I was unable to measure the altitude loss, and that's a pretty critical measurement when you're headed down.

YOU **KNOW** IT'S GOING TO BE A ROTTEN DAY WHEN —

YOU'VE JUST FINISHED PAYIN' FOR YOUR ANNUAL and YOU GET ONE OF THOSE A.D. NOTICES IN THE MAIL...

I CAN'T LOOK —

IT'S REALLY QUITE SIMPLE, KNOTHEAD. IF YOU WANT TO GO UP, PULL BACK; TO GO DOWN, PULL BACK **ALL** THE WAY!

SLOW DOWN
SPEED TRAP AHEAD

I never get lost. Everybody tells me where to go...

Here again we deal almost exclusively with ATC and controllers. The machine gun delivery of a competent tower operator is awesome, and sometimes the little airplanes, that is, general aviation types, get lost in the tangle of IFR heavy iron departures, arrivals, and clearances.

The story about the radar being inoperative was told to me as a true story, and I have no reason to believe that it isn't true. I just can't imagine, though, the full spelling of BS being used by anybody who would identify their aircraft. In any event it makes a good story.

I've injected into the last panel some pseudo names for various aircraft. Here again, I refuse to use the trade names of various products for fear of retaliation. The names shown here are thinly disguised. The Moaney 201 GQ refers to my own aircraft at the time.

EVER NOTICE HOW HARRIED SOME TOWER OPERATORS and CONTROLLERS CAN GET WHEN TRAFFIC THICKENS? WITH OTHERS, THERE'S SORT OF A FATAL-ISTIC DETACHMENT—

MOANEY 31 PAPA CLEAR-ED FOR TAKEOFF ... POOPER 2 BRAVO POP REPORT OUTER MARK-ER ...BELCHCRAFT 3 MIKE TANGO CLEARED TO LAND...AIRKNOCKER ON DOWNWIND TURN, ETC ETC

TOWER, THIS IS 31 PAPA! I'VE LOST POWER and I'M GOIN' THROUGH THE FENCE!!

SCREE

ROGER, 31 PAPA, CLEARED THROUGH THE FENCE.. BEL-CHCRAFT 3 MIKE TANGO, GO-AROUND ...POOPER 2 BRAVO POP REPORT 1 MI. FINAL, AIRKNOCKER DELAY YOUR TURN TO BASE, ETC ETC.

THEN THERE WAS AN IFR GLITCH OVER SAN DIEGO. RADAR WAS OUT and THE NATIVES UP IN THE HOLD-ING STACK WERE GETTING RESTLESS...

COME ON YOU GUYS, HURRY IT UP DOWN THERE!!

WE'RE DOIN' THE BEST WE CAN!

"B..S"!

AWRIGHT! WHICH ONE OF YOU CLODS USED B...S... ON THE AIR?

and—STARTING WITH THE TOP OF THE STACK—

POOPER 51 ALPHA, NEGATIVE ON THE B.S.!

BELCHCRAFT 21 ZEBRA, NEG-ATIVE ON THE B.S.

UNITED 12, NEGATIVE ON THE B.S.

MOANEY 201 GQ, NEGATIVE ON THE B.S.

AIR RESORT 34, NEGATIVE ON THE B.S.

AIR WEST

This particular cartoon page got me into all kinds of trouble with the lady pilots of the nation. I was lucky enough to be selected as honorary starter for the Women's Air Race Classic several years ago, and did this little number for the gals, many of whom I know personally. The handicapping gag with the brassiere streaming out behind drew a lot of fire from some of the younger lady pilot readers of our magazine. My editor was faced with a mountain of mail which stated, in effect, "I'll bet Bob Stevens wouldn't draw himself in an airplane trailing a personal item like that." There were a few subscription cancellations from those gals who felt really offended. However, I must tell the reader that the preponderance of the gals in the air race, and other women flyers of considerable notoriety and experience all came out in support of me in this particular issue when some of the nasty letters were printed in the magazine.

In answer to the challenge that I wouldn't draw myself, etc., instead of replying in written form, I drew a cartoon of myself trailing a jock strap out the cabin door. A balloon from the following plane said, "Well, that's much ado about nothing." They ran the cartoon in the Letters to the Editor section. I never heard another word after that.

IT'S ABOUT TIME WE SALUTED WOMEN PILOTS. THE AIR RACE CLASSIC FOR WOMEN LIKE ALL AIR RACES, WILL BE FRAUGHT WITH MEMORABLE EVENTS—

THE START IS ALWAYS A THRILLING SPECTACLE—

HANDICAPPING *and* A "CLEAN" BIRD ARE CRITICAL...

PINPOINT NAVIGATION IS ESSENTIAL. (*and* SPECIAL PRAYERS ARE OFFERED UP FOR TAILWINDS)

GIRLS WILL BE GIRLS—THANK HEAVENS—*and* THE FINISH HAS A DISTINCT FEMININE AIR TO IT (pun intended)!

The idea for this particular page came from Len Morgan, one of the best aviation writers in the business. Len has beaucoup experience in flying military and commercial aircraft. He writes a monthly column for *Flying Magazine*. Len had described, tongue-in-cheek, the various health hazards experienced by airline pilots in handling their daily chores. I wrote to him and asked if I could change his prose into a general aviation illustrated piece, and received an immediate "Sure, go ahead, and good luck."

The bottom half of this page contains terms which I made up that directly apply to general aviation. The "Viking Vertebrae" depicts how you'd feel after flying in one of these fine little machines for a number of hours. At the time, I owned a Viking, which had a very intimate-sized cabin. One joker was heard to describe the Viking interior as so small you had to get outside to change your mind. I loved that little old bird, though. It was fast, and Giuseppe Bellanca, who designed the airplane, was a typical Italian designer with speed on his mind. It had wooden wings which were absolutely rivetless. It's rate-of-roll approximated that of a P-51 . . . How sweet it was!

AIRMAN'S OCCUPATIONAL HEALTH HAZARDS

IF TENNIS PLAYERS CAN SUFFER AN "ELBOW", DOG SLEDDERS A "MUSHER'S KNEE" (FROM KICKING OUT BEHIND), and DANCERS A "DISCO DIGIT" (FROM SNAPPING FINGERS), SURELY THE FLYING FRATERNITY HAS ITS SHARE OF UNIQUE ACHES and PAINS—

AIRMAN'S ARM

NOTICEABLE SKELETAL CHANGE CAUSED BY CARRYING HEAVY "BRAIN BAGS". IRREVERSIBLE ARM EXTENSION.

LATIN LURCH

DISORDER COMMON TO AIRMEN RETURNING FROM VACATION SPOTS WITH QUESTIONABLE DRINKING H_2O.

SUBSONIC STOMACH

CONVICTION THAT HAMBURGER WOLFED DOWN AT "AIRPORT EATS" IS INTACT IN THE PIT ⋮URP⋮

VIKING VERTEBRAE

SEMI-PERMANENT CURVATURE CAUSED BY CLOSE QUARTERS. FOURSOMES THAT FLY TOGETHER STAY TOGETHER.

V-TAIL VERTIGO

AN ONSET OF INSTABILITY OCCASIONED BY RIDING IN THE REAR OF A POPULAR BIRD.

FED FEVER

A RAPID ELEVATION OF BODY TEMPERATURE & LOSS OF MEMORY DURING AN FAA ORAL ....

Most of this page carries its own weight. However, I must mention the Air Mech mechanic shown in the lower left-hand corner. He is a mechanic friend of mine at a nearby airport and was constantly faced with repairing a well used and beat up old crop duster. "Dusty" would drop off that klunker each evening with the admonition to have it ready to go first thing in the morning.

The kerosene lamp idea came to me as a result of looking at an advertisement in one of our popular aviation magazines in the "wish book" section. As most readers know, the "wish book" section comprises all those little one-ninth page ads clustered near the back of the magazine. They are mini-display ads that carry just enough tantalizing art on a plethora of goodies to "hook" many an airman.

"IT NEVER FAILS": AFTER REFUEL-ING AT A XC FIELD, THE ENGINE'S HOT, –YOU'RE IN A BIG HURRY TO LEAVE (A LINE SQUALL IS APPROACHING THE FIELD) – YOU HOP IN, and...

DRAT! FLOODED THE *%©!☼!

RRRRR RRRRRR RR POOP!

YOU'VE SIMPLY GOT TO STOP FLARING OUT TOO HIGH, HOSKINS!

HOW TO SEND YOUR MECH-ANIC TO THE FUNNY FARM 7

OH YEH, and I GOTTA HAVE IT BY 8 AM TOMORROW-F'SURE!

Rusty's Dusters

AIR MECH

C'MON SKINFLINT- WHY NOT BREAK DOWN and BUY A NEW LAND-ING LIGHT?!

This is a story given to me by the skywriter air advertising pilot featured. He flew from a field near the beach where his signs could be seen by all the folks sun-bathing along the strand. His story, if correct, is certainly an effective way to make your collections.

Unfortunately, this little airport is closed and I have no idea of what happened to this very fine aviator who risked his life every time he dragged one of those heavily-weighted panels off that postage-stamp sized strip.

A TRUE STORY

Reference is made to the GAR (General Aviation Reservation) system, and definitely dates this piece of art work. Those of you who were flying IFR shortly after the air controllers' (PATCO) strike will recall this rather complicated and discriminatory procedure for getting into the ATC system.

Sometimes one had to arise in the middle of the night in order to file a flight plan that the big computer in the sky would accept. It made for some pretty bleary-eyed takeoffs. The GAR system didn't have a lot of rattle room. You had ''windows'' that enabled you to get off the ground if you were not at a tower controlled airport. If you missed the ''window'' by as much as 60 seconds, the computer kicked out your flight plan and you had to go back to square one.

Because controllers were limited in the amount of area they could cover, a pilot often found himself jerked around in a rather circuitous route to get from point A to B. All in all, the system stunk, but it did the job.

SOME FOLKS ARE STILL FIGHTIN' THE GEN-GEN. AVIATION RESERVATION-SYSTEM... IT CAN BE A REAL PAIN IN THE REAR (THAT'S WHERE YOUR WALLET'S LOCATED TO PAY FUEL COSTS AFTER YOU'VE BEEN JERKED AROUND)

"**N**uggets'' was taken from the ASRS system of recording flying incidents—the *Callback* publication described earlier. Every once in a while, to enliven the otherwise grey copy matter, little bits of drollery like those on the opposite page will be dropped in to get the reader's attention.

Callback No. 1 was mailed to 3,000 recipients. Now nearly 50,000 copies go out each month. This method of aviation safety reporting has been immensely successful.

NUGGETS

• WHEN WORKING WITH PERFECT PEOPLE BE PREPARED TO FLY SOLO.

CHIRP   CHIRP   CHIRP

• I HAVE A PHOTOGRAPHIC MIND – ITS JUST THAT IT TAKES 3 DAYS TO GET THE PICTURES BACK!

• A LARGE PART OF SAFE LANDING TECHNIQUE IS KNOWING WHEN NOT TO.

• GRIEVING OVER PAST OCCURRENCES WILL NOT IMPROVE THE CURRENT STATE OF EVENTS... LEARNING FROM THEM WILL.

When a cartoonist is having one of those "blank paperitis" days and sits staring at a blank sheet before him for perhaps an hour without being smitten by an idea, he can always go back to the good old dream sequence format. It has saved the day for many a cartoonist trying to meet a deadline. In our trade, we call such formulas "evergreens."

This particular "evergreen" pictures the wildest and most humongous thing that can happen to a pilot these days. If the reader has sharp eyes, he'll note that the emergency AD that the poor recipient in the upper left-hand corner has just received calls for replacement of the entire aircraft aft of the propeller. AD's strike terror in the hearts of all owners of flying machines because, without a doubt, they are the most expensive things that can happen to you when you are operating an airplane.

Let's hear it for the controllers! Here's one that shows the other side of the pilot-controller story and has been reported to me as true.

Sometimes a student pilot just becomes overwhelmed with the fact that he is up there all alone and the grey matter doesn't swirl in the right direction. Panic or near-panic is a commodity that controllers must deal with on a daily basis.

In this particular case, our controller doesn't even start to sweat until the next to the last panel, which has got a lot to say for the steadiness of these men who work in darkened rooms miles below where we are flying.

Here we are back to communications, or the lack thereof. The old chestnuts at the top of the page have been repeated in flight ready rooms and elsewhere for decades.

   The happenstance on on the bottom sequence is one that just popped into my mind after listening to a couple of pilots commiserating over a busted check-ride. Of course, the last—or surprise—panel is the one that carries the whole story.

<u>GOOD COMMUNICATION IS NEVER HAVING TO SAY, "SAY AGAIN?"</u>

MOST PILOTS HAVE HEARD THESE OLD CHESTNUTS:

HERE'S A NEWER ONE THAT'S BOUND TO BE A CLASSIC:
TWO JOCKS ARE SHOOTIN' THE BREEZE DURING TAXI OUT and TAKEOFF —

I got the material for this page from the OX-5 Pioneers publication. For those of you too young to remember, the OX-5 organization was built around an old water-cooled engine that, appropriately enough, was labeled the OX-5. Its horsepower to weight ratio was akin to a Volkswagen engine propelling a B-17. However, it was a reliable old engine and had many devotees.

The OX-5 organization has grown into many chapters throughout the United States. The requirements for entry into this noble group of greying aviators and flying buffs is that you (1) have sometime or another in your lifetime flown an OX-5 powered aircraft (usually an old biplane), or (2) worked on this engine.

Some of the material dredged up by these old-timers is absolutely classic. I thought this particular scenario was appropriate because it used the term "Aeronaut" which is very close in its pronunciation to that of "Astronaut." There is a quantum leap between the two.

"RULES GOVERNING THE USE OF AERONAUTICAL APPARATUS"
(ACTUAL INSTRUCTIONS ISSUED WITH A 1911 PUSHER AIRCRAFT)

1." THE AERONAUT SHOULD SEAT HIMSELF IN THE APPARATUS & SECURE HIMSELF FIRMLY TO THE CHAIR BY MEANS OF THE STRAP PROVIDED."

2. OPENING THE CONTROL VALVE OF THE MOTOR, THE AERONAUT SHOULD AT THE SAME TIME GRASP THE VERTICAL STICK, OR CONTROL POLE, FOUND DIRECTLY BEFORE THE CHAIR"

... WHEN SUFFICIENT SPEED HAS BEEN ATTAINED, THE DEVICE WILL LEAVE THE GROUND & ASSUME THE POSITION OF AERONAUTICAL ASCENT, ...

... SHOULD THE AERONAUT DECIDE TO RETURN TO TERRA FIRMA, HE SHOULD CLOSE THE CONTROL VALVE OF THE MOTOR ...

... THIS WILL CAUSE THE APPARATUS TO ASSUME WHAT IS KNOWN AS THE "GLIDING POSITION", EXCEPT IN THE CASE OF THOSE MACHINES WHICH ARE INHERENTLY...

... UNSTABLE. THESE LATTER WILL ASSUME THE POSITION KNOWN AS "INVOLUNTARY SPIN" & WILL RETURN TO THE EARTH WITHOUT FURTHER ACTION ON THE PART OF THE AERONAUT" [END]

Here's another case of truth being funnier than fiction. All of those airmen who have used unicom, which is, as its name implies, universal, have had to share the airwaves with all kinds of transmissions. People order vehicles to be sent to the field, ask that home numbers be called to tell the little woman that they are "inbound," and a myriad of other seemingly minuscule tasks. Maybe it's because of this that a lot of unicom stations go unmonitored and the pilot finds himself transmitting in the blind. Personally, I don't think I'd volunteer to be a ground-bound errand boy for a continous barrage of executive requests.

Unicom is sometimes used to exchange news and views between pilots flying in the vicinity of the station and, of course, this chatter does nothing to improve the safety of air traffic flow around uncontrolled airports. The best advice one can receive on unicom is to use it as the AIM directs and for no other purpose. End of sermon.

When this page first appeared, a very close friend of mine came to me and wanted to know what the whole page was all about. You see, originally I had not encapsulated the page with what we call a ''dream balloon.'' This friend of mine could not make the transition in the last panel, so I redrew it with the dream border. (I wanted to show that our young airman was dreaming of things to be, rather than the mundane process of having to learn to fly.) My buddy still doesn't get it, I hope you do.

The student's name is Steele and I would venture to say that if I used him again in any kind of a flight sequence portrayal, I would name him ''Rocky'' Steele—that just seems to be a macho name for an up-and-coming young airman.

Here's a title that came originally from the old *Mad* magazine of great art. I saw a sequence many years ago involving a trip to a cafeteria which prompted me to use this title and direct it towards aviation. I guess this proves the point that humor spans many fields of endeavor and can be "transferred" easily.

The pictures tell the entire story. One final comment, however, is the term "Lug Nut" center. I don't know where in the world I got the term "Lug Nut," but it has served me well and I have used it in several aviation features. The natural outgrowth of the "Lug Nut" center or corporation or whatever (in these days of raider takeovers) would be "Mr. Big Wrench."

WHAT'S WORSE THAN...?

General Aviation News or GAN—"The Green Sheet" for short—is a well known aviation bi-weekly. Mr. Daryl Murphy, the editor of GAN, came up with this auto/aircraft analogy in one of his editorials. I have been letting GAN use my material for a number of years and thought it only fair to reciprocate by stealing some of their material. I called Daryl to get his permission to convert his words to pictures. You are looking at the result.

There are more analogies to be drawn—particularly in the heavy iron category. Since most of us can only dream of having a Lear or Citation, I kept the subject low-key.

AUTO/AIRCRAFT ANALOGY QUIZ

SEE IF YOU CAN MATCH THE AIRCRAFT *and* ITS AUTOMOTIVE COUNTERPART.
(CAUTION: THIS QUIZ IS FULL OF SWEEPING GENERALITIES)

MATCH THE BIRD WITH THE DESCRIPTION
(ANSWERS BELOW)

A.

1. "LIKE A BUICK, A CADILLAC OR A LINCOLN — DISTINCTIVE, STYLISH, A BIT CONSERVATIVE & OLD FASHIONED, LIKE A RICH MAIDEN AUNT."

B.

2. "THE CHEVROLET/PONTIAC/OLDS OF FLYING — AS RELIABLE *and* FAMILIAR AS THE FAMILY DOCTOR. UBIQUITOUS. AS NUMEROUS AS STRUGGLING ATTORNEYS!"

C.

3. "A CULT FOLLOWING LIKE PORSCHE OR LOTUS OWNERS. THESE OWNERS DON'T PUBLICLY BRAG ABOUT THEIR AIRPLANES AS MUCH AS OWNERS OF OTHER MAKES — THEY WANT TO KEEP THEIR DISCOVERY IN THE FAMILY"

D.

4. "THOUGHTFUL, FRIENDLY, COURTEOUS, KIND, THRIFTY, OBEDIENT; REMINISCENT OF A FORD OR A DODGE — OR PERHAPS A DE SOTO"

ANSWERS (FEEL FREE TO DISAGREE) **A-2, B-4, C-1, D-3**

Here's another gem from "*On the Air*," the IFR monthly publication. All of these incidents are supposed to be true reports. I can really empathize with the instructor in this particular situation because I instructed for a number of years and there were some students you'd just rather not have anybody else know you were instructing.

On this same subject, one time a student and I reached takeoff power on the takeoff roll, and I yelled "takeoff power" to indicate, of course, that we had reached the proper amount of manifold pressure. His immediate response was, of course, to cut the power. Fortunately, we had a long runway to stop on.

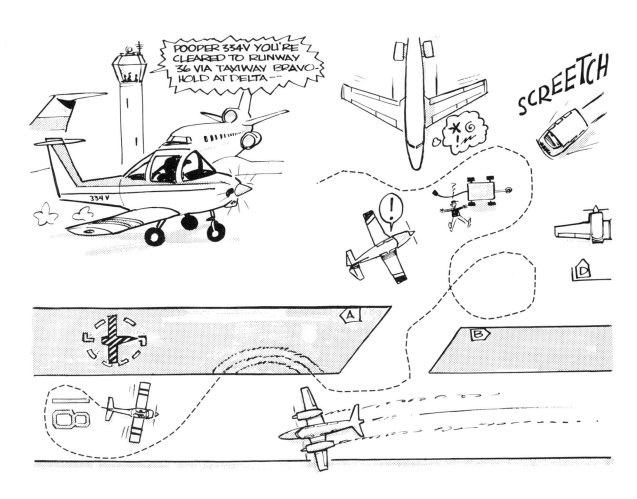

I haven't the faintest idea where the title for the material on the next two pages came from, but obviously it was from an aviation publication. I would love to give the credit where it is due but I cannot remember, nor can I find it in my files. Everything on this page and the one that follows can happen and has happened to many aviators and their sometimes reluctant passengers.

The drawing in the lower right-hand corner is one of those never-do situations that we spoke about earlier in the book. Busted minimums can mean a busted aircraft, people, and egos.

Continuing with the greatest "fibs," the only thing that is worthy of note in this particular panel is the fellow who has the wrong traffic in sight (which occurs frequently in our crowded skies) and the portrayal of the FAA in a prosecuting "mode." Unfortunately, it's become a game of cops and robbers between the FAA and the active pilot. I have attended several meetings recently where the discussion among pilots is *not* how FAA can help them but how to avoid being written up by "the Sam Spades of the Sky." It's a sad commentary on the way things are shaping up for the general aviation pilot.

AVIATION'S GREATEST FIBS (CONT.) -

"I ONLY NEED GLASSES FOR READING"

"DON'T WORRY ABOUT WT. and BALANCE - IT'LL FLY"

"I'VE GOT THE TRAFFIC IN SIGHT"

"I *KNOW* THE GEAR WAS DOWN!"

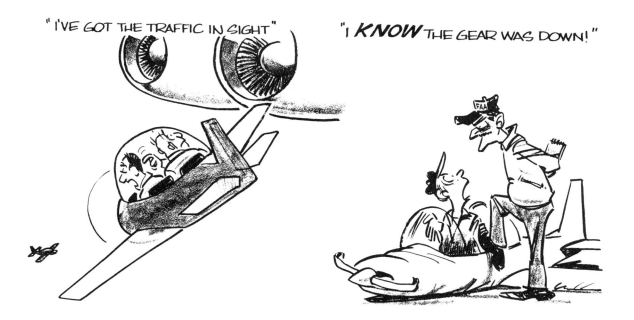

Here's more of the "What's Worse Than . . .?" material. I call the reader's attention to the lower right-hand corner. The gobbledygook copy that you see being transmitted from ATC is a marvelous artist's aid. This is what is known in the trade as "false copy" and it is used in advertising layout merely to indicate what printed copy in block form will look like. This stuff can be bought by the sheet and I have used it in numerous occasions to represent words spoken to a recipient by someone who is either (1) speaking in Sanskrit, or (2) speaking at near the speed of sound.

WHAT'S WORSE THAN...?

No aviation book—particularly one addressed to pilots—would be complete without *Ten Rules of Aviation*. The origin of these pearls of wisdom is lost to antiquity . . . yet the message is as current as today's TV news. These rules rate with the ode, *Why I Want to be a Pilot* as aviator classics. Rule 3 is as old as Icarus—5 through 9 came after blind flight and the FAA.

No one, repeat no one who pilots a flying machine can argue with the logic of rule 8, e.g., given the choice, would you rather ram a blockhouse or an outhouse?

Feel free to copy this page and paste it on your instrument panel.

TEN RULES OF AVIATION

1. Do not bust your butt.

2. Do not let anyone else bust your butt for you.

3. Remember the pilot is always the first to arrive at the scene of the accident.

4. If in doubt – get out!

5. In instrument flying one peek at the ground is worth a thousand crosschecks.

6. Thunderstorms and ice are just like being pregnant – there is no such thing as just a little.

7. Remember airplanes fly because of Bernoulli not Marconi (e.g. don't drop the aircraft to fly the mike).

8. If a crash is inevitable hit the softest, cheapest thing you can find as slowly as possible.

9. What you don't say you don't have to take back at the hearing.

10. Don't forget rule one!

The genesis of this sequence of drawings was the United States Air Force. I experienced this particular type of dry humor when landing with an old codger easily double my age back in early cadet days. This fellow was a colonel who had very poor eyesight; people would have to draw short straws to see who was going to fly with the old geezer. He made the most terrible landings possible and they were in a tail-dragger, which made the porpoising effect even more pronounced.

In the Air Force situation, the question, "Did you notice what time I landed?" was made by the colonel to the tower, and the tower broadcast the reply to anyone with a receiver within a radius of about 40 miles. The air was filled with gales of laughter and snide remarks—none of which registered with the colonel, who was also hard-of hearing.

Some of the radio transmissions between aircraft and the tower are truly remarkable. The case depicted here was one that an experienced instructor heard while flying in our local area.

The querulous woman in the lower panel is typical of a person (probably on a first flight) who is undergirding her terror by a continual barrage of talk. I've flown many hours with this type of person and there's absolutely no way to shut them off except to climb to altitude and let them go to sleep. An altitude between 10,000 and 12,000 feet has a tendency to quiet folks down.

The engine stoppage blurb and comment is very personal to me. I decided one time to give my new bride a ride in a rather decrepit airplane. Sure enough, as soon as we got to pattern altitude, the old mill started to die. I was frantically looking for a place to plant the bird when the wife yelled at me angrily, "Bob! Stop fooling around!"

HOWZAT AGAIN? (TRUE STORIES) DEPT.

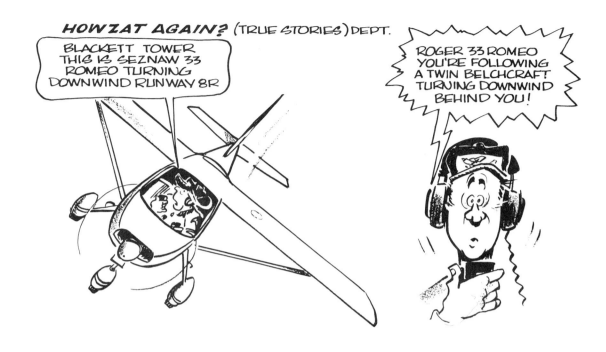

THEN THERE WAS THE QUERULOUS LADY ON HER VERY FIRST FLIGHT—

$\mathbf{I}$ drew this page while living in the "Great Northwet." I don't know what got into us, but we decided to move up into the Northwest and live on an island. The weather was atrocious most of the time and my flying was greatly hampered by the low visibility, icing, and all the other good things that go with a rapid frontal passage. The few days I did get to fly, there were not many other folks out. You see, the island on which we lived was not exactly a roaring metropolis, at 1,800 souls in the winter. We had, however, very nice airport facilities and I had a hangar for the first time in my civilian pilot flying career.

Coincidentally with our living in this damp place, the old joints didn't work as smoothly as they used to and I had a lot of trouble getting the plane in and out of the hangar. It never failed that when I was ready to push her back, there would not be one soul visible on the airport to lend a hand.

PUTTING THE BIRD AWAY

THOSE READERS WHO'RE FORTUNATE ENOUGH TO FIND – and CAN AFFORD – HANGARS SOON LEARN THERE'S MORE TO PUTTING A PLANE AWAY THAN OPENING THE DOOR(S) and SHOVING IT IN!

1. THE GROSS WT. OF YOUR SINGLE JUMPS TO THAT OF A 747 THE MINUTE YOU PUT A TOWBAR ON IT –

2. NO MATTER HOW CAREFULLY YOU PAINT WHEEL GUIDE LINES, YOU CAN ALWAYS FOUL IT UP!

3. THE DAY YOU GIVE UP and HAVE TO ASK FOR HELP, THERE ISN'T A SOUL IN SIGHT FOR MILES ...

4. FINALLY, YOU BREAK DOWN and BUY A FANCY POWER TOWBAR, BUT DON'T READ THE INSTRUCTIONS

The title of this page comes from a well-known series in other publications. I have adapted it to general aviation. As anyone knows who has rented an aircraft, being the keeper of a key can cost you many extra dollars per day when you walk off with it.

The comment about weather people laughing when you say, "I'd like to go to VFR," rarely occurs with competent FAA personnel. The briefings that you get over the telephone are generally quite good. However, the briefer will rarely volunteer any information that is benign in nature. For example, one time I asked about the temperature/dew point spread when being briefed and was told that it was at least 5 degrees so it was unlikely that there would be any fog en route. However, upon arriving at my destination, the briefer had failed to mention the fact that *every* day in the past several weeks the temperature and dew point had come together usually after 4 p.m. This resulted in a near zero-zero approach, which still gives me the clanks as I think about it five years afterwards.

YOU *KNOW* IT'S GOING TO BE A ROTTEN DAY WHEN...

YOU WAKE UP & DISCOVER YOUR WATERBED BROKE – THEN REALIZE YOU DON'T HAVE A WATERBED...

IN PUTTING ON YOUR CLOTHES YOU FIND THE KEYS TO LAST WEEK'S RENTAL BIRD –

YOU PUT BOTH CONTACT LENSES IN ONE EYE...

WHEN YOU CALL WX and SAY "VFR" and HEAR GALES OF LAUGHTER...

YOU WANNA GO **WHERE?**

YOU FINISH A 30 MIN. PRE-FLIGHT and THEY SWITCH PLANES ON YOU –

AS YOU TAXI OUT, FIRE and RESCUE EQUIPMENT LINE THE RUNWAY!

FIRE DEPT. AMBULANCE

In our computerized micro-miniature era—brought on largely by space flight technology—the voice activated instrument has become more or less commonplace in heavy equipment, that it, airliners. The thing that set this whole page off was the instrument that is now required in all airliners that commands the pilot to "pull up!" when the ground proximity radar depicts a minimum altitude condition. I thought about this voice activated instrument for a while and then imagined what would happen if we applied the same verbal warnings to other equipment in our birds.

Actually, for the last three or four decades, we have had GCA in the military, which is, as you know, a person talking you down (as shown in the ILS blurb). After reaching a certain minimum altitude, the voice at the other end will tell you, "You have reached minimums, take over and land visually." On several occasions, I've still been in the solid soup at this point and going around is the better part of valor. It never seems to fail, however, that once committed to go-around, the runway will hove into sight after it's too late to do anything about it!

IMAGINE VOICE-ACTIVATED SYSTEMS TIED INTO VARIOUS COMPONENTS OF SMALL GEN. AVIATION AIRCRAFT. THE POSSIBILITIES ARE ENDLESS:

AIRSPEED -

"IT SOUNDS LIKE YOUR MOTHER'S IN THE REAR SEAT!"

ALTITUDE -

TRANSPONDER -

ILS

NOW, JUST IMAGINE ALL OF 'EM GOING AT THE SAME TIME!

Here's good old "lug-nut" again. In this particular case, we have a controller bailing out a befuddled student once more. Here, the student is so near the edge of panic that the only thing that makes any sense to him is the compass.

Speaking of compasses, an old timer in flying can still make an error with this little jewel. It happened to me and a planeload of my friends coming back from the Northwest. I tried to land according to my compass heading in a largely blacked out area at night. The compass had hung up in a given position quite a few degrees off of the runway heading and I had been at altitude just long enough to be slightly woozy. The tower and I argued for at least three or four minutes before I caved in and accepted his diagnosis that I was on the wrong heading. Needless to say, the landing was made safely, but I changed compasses shortly thereafter.

This is a direct steal from work I did previously in an RV magazine. Now when a cartoonist takes one of his own ideas and converts it to another field, that is legitimate. The cartoonist code strictly forbids outright plagiarism of someone else's material. However, you can make what we call a "legitimate switch."

I drew some fire on this from the ladies again. I just don't know what it is about women in aviation. I have had a terrible time trying to please the distaff element. It must be that I'm a latent misogynist (misogyny, n. - hatred of women). That can't be true, I really *like* women—as my two ex-wives will attest.

The story about the two jokesters turning off their transponders was relayed to me at a convention of Mooney pilots. The storyteller swears that the situation actually occurred down in Florida, I believe. Personally, I think it's a dirty trick; however, some pilots are driven to extremes by overbearing controllers.

The fellow propping the aircraft was taken from a book by Martin Leeuwis, a very good friend of mine from the Netherlands. Martin depicted the situation in an entirely different manner and therefore this becomes a legitimate switch. Martin, himself, is quite an unusual pilot and character. He flew as a Dutch fighter pilot for a number of years and used to sell my books all over Europe by cramming them in the back of his Dutch jet fighter. He later wrote his own books and is now a first officer aboard a KLM airliner.

This action was alleged to have occurred in the L.A. sector one night during a rapid cold front passage. L.A., because of its size, is rife with aviation communication stories. The best one I think I ever heard from this area was the story about the controller who directed a Piper aircraft flying at 9,000 feet to climb immediately to 11,000 feet for "noise abatement." When the flabbergasted pilot asked about noise abatement at nearly two miles of altitude, the controller shot back, "Well, if you meet that twin coming at you at the same altitude, it's going to make one hellofaracket!"

The next two pages are the direct result of going to a Mooney Aircraft Pilots Association (MAPA) convention in Kerrville, Texas, where the Mooney aircraft owners and pilots meet each year at a "homecoming" bash. A bunch of us got on the stage and put four chairs in the approximate position of the seats in a Mooney and proceeded to go through an act—completely impromptu—on how to get in and out of an aircraft with one door on it. It turned into one hilarious skit.

The fellow in the lower right-hand corner would be, if drawn correctly, Roy LoPresti, the famed aircraft designer who had been chief engineer at Mooney. Roy has now moved on to other companies in ever increasing stature as one of the best aircraft engineers in the United States. His sense of humor was nearly as good as his aircraft design work.

THERE'S A WHOLE BUNCH OF WAYS TO BOARD AN AIRPLANE WITH A SINGLE DOOR OVER THE WING—HERE ARE JUST A FEW:

THE "BACK-IN-IMPALE-YOUR-FANNY" TECHNIQUE

THE "CRAWL-ACROSS-and-ROTATE" METHOD (PILOTS)

THE "I-COULD-USE-ANOTHER-HAND" SPLITZ.

THE "IF-ALL-SEATS-ARE-FULL" LAST DITCH MANUEVER (PILOTS)

We continue the story started on the previous page. There are a couple of things here that you might note. One is that I have used all males (as previously explained) because women getting in and out of airplanes can be quite a sight and rather degrading if observed from the wrong angle. I know that in our particular model aircraft where you load over the wing, my wife always wore a pair of slacks to get in and out of the airplane because there just is no way to do it gracefully in a skirt.

Once four people are firmly belted down in a small four-place aircraft, there isn't a whole lot of room left and I don't care whether it's a light twin or a big single, the dimensions are usually fairly restricted—so restricted in some models that the expression, "You have to get outside to change your mind" holds very true. I actually experienced the situation shown in the lower right-hand corner and it extended our stay on the ground a full 15 minutes. As the old expression goes, "If you have time to spare, go by air," applies here.

"HOW TO GET IN and OUT OF A 4-PLACE AIRCRAFT WITH A SINGLE DOOR" PART II

THE "ABC" METHOD (VERY COMMON). OK ONLY IF THE PILOT BOARDS FIRST!

THE DEMOCRATIC "WE'LL DRAW STRAWS TO SEE WHO SITS IN THE BACK" PROCESS.

ONCE ABOARD, CONSIDERABLE SKILL MUST BE EXERCISED TO KEEP FROM MAIMING REAR-SEAT PASSENGERS WHEN ADJUSTING THE FRONT SEATS —

AND, FINALLY, AFTER EVERYONE'S IN POSITION and STRAPPED DOWN:

There is no louder silence than that of a dead engine in a single-engine aircraft. It is so quiet that you can usually hear your heart trying to beat its way out of your chest. This situation, i.e., having the engine stop, has occurred to me three times in my private flying career. In each case, however, the cause for the stoppage was of my own doing—I had failed to change the fuel tank selector at the proper time. The expletives used by my passengers would fill a small book and my wife came up with some rather creative new tea party language.

On this same trip, our return was uneventful because the three passengers had pooled their resources and purchased a big alarm clock that was hung around my neck. It went off at the appropriate intervals to remind me to transfer tanks. How humiliatin'

The following two pages fall into the category of flying safety and as any pilot will recognize, it is very thinly disguised as humor. This is the type of drawing that, if you can pull it off, someone might get a little chuckle out of the proceedings. However, the object lesson learned might stick with them a lot longer.

The fellow flying under the overcast through the pine trees was used by numerous FAA publications (on a gratis basis, of course) to show readers what can happen to you when you let the airplane get too far out in front of you.

HOW TO THOROUGHLY SCARE YOURSELF IN AN AIRPLANE:

RUN A FUEL TANK DRY [1].

GET BUSY IN THE COCKPIT and NEGLECT YOUR SKY SCAN [2].

1. BONUS PUCKER POINTS GIVEN WHEN IN IFR CONDITIONS.

2. REMEMBER: REPORT ALL NEAR MID-AIRS! (AFTER YOU'VE CHANGED YOUR DRAWERS, OF COURSE)

TAKE THE BAIT ON A SUCKER HOLE and HAVE IT GO FROM ⦾ TO ⊕ [3].

RUN OUT OF ALTITUDE, ESCAPE ROUTES and IDEAS ALL AT THE SAME TIME [4].

3. YOU NEEDN'T REPORT THIS—THE FAA WILL DO IT FOR YOU.

4. THIS WILL ALSO PROBABLY BE REPORTED FOR YOU—BY YOUR NEWSPAPER.

Continuing on the same theme of flying safety, of all the situations depicted on this page, I think the one on the lower right-hand corner is the one that has caused more grief than any other situation shown. The loud rush of air as the door goes into the "trail" position is scarier than it is dangerous. Most aircraft have a procedure for pulling the door closed again by slowing up and making a slight turn in the direction of the open door. It's a situation that catches people by surprise and creates the greatest havoc.

Here again the situation of the fellow taking off with the trim in the full nose-up position actually happened to me. The aircraft belonged to a friend of mine who wanted to take some aerial photographs and asked me to fly his bird. He had left the trim in the full nose-up on landing and then asked me to take it over. The error was mine for not checking the trim setting before takeoff and I, suffice to say, will never repeat *that* situation! It's pretty scary to be going almost straight up with minimum air speed.

IN A RETRACTABLE, GRAB THE GEAR HANDLE INSTEAD OF THE FLAPS ON ROLLOUT:

IN A TWIN, START THE LEFT ENGINE AFTER CLEARING THE RIGHT:

TAKEOFF WITH THE ELEVATOR TRIM IN THE FULL NOSE-UP POSITION:

...and THIS ONE SEEMS THE HAIRIEST-TAKE OFF WITH THE CABIN DOOR UNLATCHED!

This story was related to me by ''Old Bill,'' a good old boy at a local air-port. He claims that this actually happened to him in his student days. It's rare now to find a Chew Mail Pouch Tobacco ad on any building, so that's gotta' tell you that this is an old, old story.

The teller of this tale has a little mini-biplane that is an absolute ter-ror to land in a crosswind. Some of the most thrilling days of my life have been watching him actually plant this airplane on a very narrow runway with about a 25 knot crosswing. Believe it or not, ''Old Bill'' is still among the living.

When a reader sees this kind of a treatment from a cartoonist, you can assume one of two things. He has either reached the complete end of his creativity string or he has blown a gasket. It occurred to me that the balloons could be made into something other than just a round or oblong blob. I have used this treatment in several other types of cartoon illustration and the only trouble I've ever had with the symbols is to describe what the outline represents—some editors are pretty dense.

The blowhard in the center of the picture relating flying to sailing was overheard by my wife and me on a trip between two of the Hawaiian Islands. The helmsman—a macho man—was telling a cluster of female admirers around him that this was the way one flew an airplane. I sidled up to him after the crowd thinned down and asked him how much flying time he had and he candidly admitted, "Oh, I've been reading about it."

You will recall a few pages back when we discussed "Old Bill" and his biplane; this story also came from Bill. He likes to tell it as a true story, and I don't doubt one bit that the FAA could pull such a stunt. Nowadays, the cops and robbers attitude between the FAA inspectors and pilots has gotten to the point where this occurrence is more the rule than the exception.

It's too bad, but it's true . . . many of the young pilots I have known who have gone into FAA work have become fire-breathing dragons as soon as they get their certification. It seems as though the course that they take back there in Oklahoma City was outlined by Attila the Hun. Just listen to the lectures that they give to pilots who step out of line.

This is absolutely the last aviation glossary blurb you will see in this book, I promise it.

The dialogue in the upper right-hand corner from the airline pilot is unfortunately quite true. Whenever such an exchange takes place you will, unfortunately, be reading about it in the next morning's paper. It just seems that some of these guys feel they can walk on water. Recent events in the air transportation weather detection business have indicated that wind shear can bring down even the biggest of birds and new equipment is being devised to warn incoming planes of this phenomenon.

I used the little guy upside down between cloud decks in the lower left-hand corner in a cartoon caption contest. It just seemed to me that mentioning the time was very appropriate; particularly when one considers being upside down that close to the ground.

You KNOW IT'S GOING TO BE A BAD DAY WHEN YOU R.O.N. & AWAKE TO THE A.M. WEATHER ONLY TO FIND THEY'RE SHOWING EMERGENCY ROUTES OUT OF THE CITY—

AT THE AIRPORT YOU HEAR THIS EXCHANGE—

AIRLINE 123, CLEARED TO LAND; WIND 270 AT 25, GUSTS TO 30, HEAVY RAIN, HAIL, SEVERE SHEER BELOW 300 FT, RVR 2400 FT.

AH, ROGER, 123 IS CLEARED TO LAND—and, AH, LET US KNOW IF IT GETS ANY WORSE.

GEEZ! IT'S LATER THAN I THOUGHT!

AVIATION GLOSSARY

"CIRCLE-TO-LAND"

AN ATC PHRASE WHICH MEANS, (1) "FIND THE AIRPORT IF YOU CAN" OR, (2) REFERS TO FLYING THE OBSTACLE COURSE AROUND AIRPORTS AFTER BEING LUCKY ENOUGH TO FIND THE PLACE IFR (I FOLLOW ROADS)

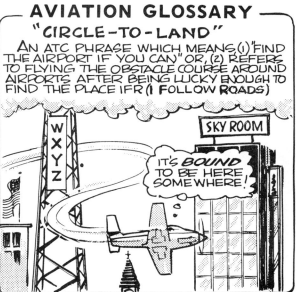

SKY ROOM

IT'S *BOUND* TO BE HERE SOMEWHERE!

The gag in the upper left-hand corner is strictly a word gag. The Short Sunderland is an ungainly looking flying boxcar. They are used anywhere a heavy load has to be transported in a not-too-rapid fashion.

Regarding the guy that landed on the highway, the story stems from a report of a Mooney that landed on the highway between Winslow and Gallup, New Mexico, minus a prop. The pilot picked a stretch that was not occupied by automobiles, landed safely, and pulled over to the side in a parking area. The Arizona Highway Patrol came up and, of course, the first thing the patrolman asked for was the pilot's driver's license.

Since I draw for family audiences, I could not put the appropriate four-letter word under the drawing in the lower left-hand corner. It doesn't leave much to the imagination, however, to guess what it is.

"HOWZAT AGIN?" DEPT:

MOANEY 201 GQ YOU ARE NO.3 TO LAND BEHIND A PAIR OF SHORTS!

SITUATION: A POOR SOUL HAS DEADSTICKED ONTO AN INTERSTATE.

HEY, YOU GOT TO SEE WHAT OL' SMOKEY'S PULLED OVER ON SLAB I-5!

"...OH FUDGE!"

EVER WONDER...

HOW HELICOPTERS MAKE INSTRUMENT APPROACHES?

WHOP WHOP WHOP

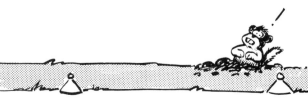

When I looked at this page while assembling the book, it occurred to me that every situation I had drawn on the page involved a prop. As all pilots know, props can be very dangerous things and it is difficult to treat them lightly.

One of the drawings is taken directly from my friend Martin Leeuwis's book (the one-legged individual cranking a prop on an old biplane). Martin's sense of humor takes a strange twist now and again—I thought this had a touch of ''sick humor,'' but the facial expression kept it from becoming macabre.

The Piper Cub used on this page brings back many memories of my early flying days. I flew the 40 horsepower (actually it was 37 horse-power) model in the early days of World War II, and flying only in the desert areas away from our defended coastline, it was not uncommon to be passed by trucks and even small vehicles while at full throttle with the J-2 Cub. Boy, that little airplane was fun to fly! There are thousands upon thousands of World War II pilots who cut their teeth on the little yellow bird.

WITH THE UPSURGE IN HOME-BUILTS, ULTRA LIGHTS and ANTIQUES THE ART OF HAND PROPPING HAS COME A FULL CIRCLE SINCE THE 30'S (WHEN 'SELF-STARTERS' REFERRED TO THE PILOT)

There are three things that illustrators can be assured will draw attention. (1) A gal in minimum attire, (2) kids, and (3) puppy dogs. You'll note that I managed to get two of the three into this panel. Who can argue with the love of a puppy dog for his master and the guy who feeds him.

We have some flying friends who refuse to go anywhere without their huge Walt Disney-type dog aboard. When they unload at the ramp at their destination, it creates quite a stir to see this behemoth of a dog unload from the rear seat, bounce down on the ramp, and look for the nearest bush. They are quite a couple, and the dog is a friend of anyone who smells like an airplane.

The captions for these little ditties were written by a very talented free-lance author and appeared in *AG-Pilot International*. I merely added the illustrations to the obvious fabrications of the truth. We have covered what most of these situations will do to you in the flying game earlier in this book.

I like the scenario regarding the use of radios. I've violated every one of these. I would like to meet and shake the hand of any person who could sign this document as a true and correct statement. He belongs in a category *far* above the everyday pilot.

IN ALL MY HOURS OF FLYING, I HAVE **NEVER:**

EXCEEDED GROSS WEIGHT

BUSTED MINIMUMS

LEFT MY CHARTS AT HOME OR AT THE AIRPORT.

FAILED TO GET WX FORECASTS

IN USING THE RADIOS:

- ASKED," WAS THAT FOR ME"?
- TURNED THE CDI "TO"INSTEAD OF"FROM".
- FAILED TO IDENT THE STATION.
- USED THE WRONG FREQUENCY.
- INADVERTANTLY TURNED OFF THE VHF.

MADE A BAD LANDING—

I CERTIFY THE ABOVE IS A TRUE and CORRECT STATEMENT—

SIGNED _____
(1ST FIBBER)

ATTEST _____
(2ND FIBBER)

NOTE: IN THE EVENT OF A TIE, DUPLICATE HALOS WILL BE AWARDED. ALSO THE DECISION OF THE FINAL JUGDE (and WE ALL KNOW WHO *THAT* IS!) IS *FINAL!*

The delightfully humorous captions for this page were taken from that great document published by the Confederate Air Force entitled simply, *"Aviation Glossary."* The CAF, as many know, is a grand bunch of folks headquartered down in Texas who are keeping the heritage of World War II aircraft alive. They do this by performing air shows throughout the country and by maintaining a fleet of aircraft of that era—1941 to 1945.

The Confederate Air Force acknowledges that this material, which you see depicted in art form here, has been "stolen from only the very best sources." That should give you some idea as to the seriousness of their whole publishing business.

EVER WONDER WHAT PARTS and SUNDRY ITEMS MAKE UP THAT FLYING MACHINE STRAPPED TO YOUR GLUTEUS MAXIMUS? HERE'S A CUT-AWAY VIEW OF A MODERN BIRD (NOMENCLATURE COURTESY OF THE CONFEDERATE A.F.)*

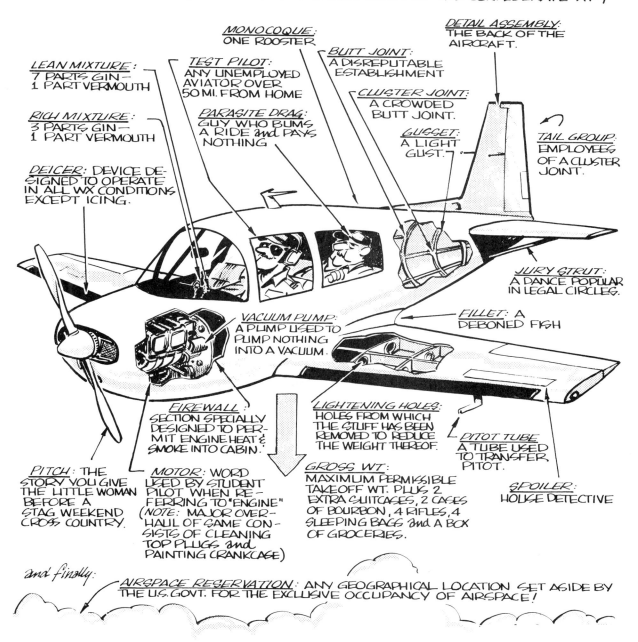

MONOCOQUE: ONE ROOSTER

DETAIL ASSEMBLY: THE BACK OF THE AIRCRAFT.

BUTT JOINT: A DISREPUTABLE ESTABLISHMENT

TEST PILOT: ANY UNEMPLOYED AVIATOR OVER 50 MI. FROM HOME

LEAN MIXTURE: 7 PARTS GIN — 1 PART VERMOUTH

CLUSTER JOINT: A CROWDED BUTT JOINT.

RICH MIXTURE: 3 PARTS GIN — 1 PART VERMOUTH

PARASITE DRAG: GUY WHO BUMS A RIDE and PAYS NOTHING

GUSSET: A LIGHT GUST.

TAIL GROUP: EMPLOYEES OF A CLUSTER JOINT.

DEICER: DEVICE DESIGNED TO OPERATE IN ALL WX CONDITIONS EXCEPT ICING.

JURY STRUT: A DANCE POPULAR IN LEGAL CIRCLES.

FILLET: A DEBONED FISH

VACUUM PUMP: A PUMP USED TO PUMP NOTHING INTO A VACUUM.

FIREWALL: SECTION SPECIALLY DESIGNED TO PERMIT ENGINE HEAT & SMOKE INTO CABIN.

LIGHTENING HOLES: HOLES FROM WHICH THE STUFF HAS BEEN REMOVED TO REDUCE THE WEIGHT THEREOF.

PITOT TUBE: A TUBE USED TO TRANSFER PITOT.

PITCH: THE STORY YOU GIVE THE LITTLE WOMAN BEFORE A STAG WEEKEND CROSS COUNTRY.

MOTOR: WORD USED BY STUDENT PILOT WHEN REFERRING TO "ENGINE" (NOTE: MAJOR OVERHAUL OF SAME CONSISTS OF CLEANING TOP PLUGS and PAINTING CRANKCASE)

GROSS WT: MAXIMUM PERMISSIBLE TAKEOFF WT. PLUS 2 EXTRA SUITCASES, 2 CASES OF BOURBON, 4 RIFLES, 4 SLEEPING BAGS and A BOX OF GROCERIES.

SPOILER: HOUSE DETECTIVE

and finally:

AIRSPACE RESERVATION: ANY GEOGRAPHICAL LOCATION SET ASIDE BY THE U.S. GOVT. FOR THE EXCLUSIVE OCCUPANCY OF AIRSPACE!

* THEY REPORT THAT THESE TERMS HAVE BEEN STOLEN FROM ONLY THE MOST AUTHENTIC PUBLICATIONS

This little story uses a couple of my favorite people in it. The editor of *Private Pilot* and his wife, Elizabeth, both have tickets and swap off their flying from time to time. I won't say that Dennis looks like this individual, but he certainly has contributed to my happiness over the years by being a genuinely good fellow, fine pilot, and a fellow QB member.

Elizabeth, besides being a good pilot, has her A&P mechanic's license, and whenever these folks get away from their home base and get into trouble, Elizabeth can usually diagnose the problem and fix it in short order. As a matter of fact, Liz saved my bacon on at least one occasion when she found dirty oil rags left over from a previous inspection wrapped around my exhaust pipe. All in all, they are quite a couple.

We end the book, appropriately, with fouled-up communications. These gems came from a publication entitled simply *IFR*. It is a smallish magazine aimed at the IFR-rated pilot. I'm sure its circulation will grow as the numbers of instrument pilots increase . . . and increase they must if people are to fly in the ever more complex world of navaids and controlled airspace.

I'm not going to say *another* word about controllers and the FAA. But, wouldn't it be great if a pilot could just walk out, pre-flight his plane and fly *directly* to some delightful place of his own choosing unhindered by radios, TCAs, TRSAs, MOAs, VORs, ARSAs, etc., etc.? Just for a little while, maybe?

MIKE MISCUES

With all the new controlled airspace, the following true exchange between an aircraft and approach control may become commonplace ... *unfortunately.*